Maths

Rapid Tests 6

Rebecca Brant

Schofield & Sims

Introduction

This book gives you practice in answering mathematics questions quickly.

The questions are like the questions on the 11+ and other school selection tests. You must find the correct answers.

School selection tests are usually timed, so you need to get used to working quickly. Each test has a target time for you to work towards. You should time how long you spend on each test, or you can ask an adult to time you.

What you need

- A pencil
- An eraser
- A ruler
- A protractor
- A clock, watch or stopwatch
- A sheet of rough paper
- An adult to help you work out how long you take and to mark the test for you

What to do

- Turn to **Section 1 Test 1** on page 4. Look at the grey box at the top of the page labelled **Target time**. This tells you how long the test should take.
- When you are ready to start, write down the time or start the stopwatch. Or the adult helping you will tell you to begin.
- Read each question carefully and then write the answer on the answer line. Sometimes you need to draw your answer in the space instead. You should not use a calculator.
- Try to answer every question. If you do get stuck on a question, leave it and go on to the next one. Work quickly and try your best.
- When you reach the end, stop. Write down the time or stop the stopwatch. Or tell the adult that you have finished.
- With the adult, work out how long you took to do the test. Fill in the **Time taken** box at the end of the test.
- The adult will mark your test and fill in the **Score** and **Target met?** boxes.
- Turn to the **Progress chart** on page 40. Write your score in the box and colour in the graph to show how many questions you got right.
- Did you get some questions wrong? You should always have another go at them before you look at the answers. Then ask the adult to check your work and help you if you are still not sure.
- When you have finished working through this book, and are able to answer the questions both rapidly and correctly, you will be well prepared for school selection tests.

Published by **Schofield & Sims Ltd**,
7 Mariner Court, Wakefield, West Yorkshire WF4 3FL, UK
Telephone 01484 607080
www.schofieldandsims.co.uk

This edition copyright © Schofield & Sims Ltd, 2018
First published in 2018
Second impression 2019

Author: **Rebecca Brant**. Rebecca Brant has asserted her moral rights under the Copyright, Designs and Patents Act, 1988, to be identified as the author of this work.

British Library Cataloguing in Publication Data. A catalogue record for this book is available from the British Library.

Design by **Ledgard Jepson Ltd**
Front cover design by **Ledgard Jepson Ltd**
Printed in the UK by **Page Bros (Norwich) Ltd**

ISBN 978 07217 1426 4

Contents

A **pull-out answers section** (pages A1 to A20) appears in the centre of this book, between pages 20 and 21. It also gives simple guidance on how best to use this book. Remove this section before the child begins working through the tests.

Target time: **8 minutes**

1. Solve these calculations.

    a) 74 684 657 + 35 834 345 =

    _____

    b) 45 936 635 − 32 607 832 =

    _____

    c) _____ ÷ 3 = 544

    d) 345 × 67 =   _____

    e) (5 × 2)² + (30 ÷ 6) =   _____

2. Three ferries sail from an island to the mainland at midday each day.

    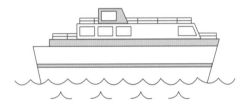

    One day, 2472 people want to travel and are split equally between the ferries. How many passengers did each ferry carry?   _____

3. Amy is 6 years younger than her sister. The product of their ages is 135. How old is Amy?   _____

4. I think of a number. I divide it by 7 then add 3 and the answer is 14. What was my number?   _____

5. Mia has to make 5 dozen cupcakes for a wedding. So far she has made 36. How many more does she have left to make?   _____

6. A school had 1415 students. Last Monday, 237 were absent. How many students were at school?   _____

7. What is the sum of the first 5 cubed numbers?   _____

8. In an aquarium there are 4710 fish. They are shared equally between 314 tanks. How many fish are there in each tank?   _____

9. Solve these division sums and write any remainders as fractions.

    a) 4557 ÷ 7 =   _____

    b) $2\ 4\overline{)1\ \ 2\ \ 8\ \ 5}$ _____

10. Write the missing rules for these function machines.

    7 → | × 3 | → | a) | → | ÷ 4 | → 6

    a) _____

    4 → | × 5 | → | b) | → | ÷ 3 | → 9

    b) _____

11. What is the smallest number that can be divided by 3, 4, 5 and 6 exactly?   _____

12. What is the product of 0.03 and 12?   _____

13. Damian works as a car salesman. He earns £1200 a month plus £50 for each car he sells.

    a) How much will he earn in a month if he sells 14 cars?   _____

    b) How many cars would he have to sell to earn £2450?   _____

Score: _____   Time taken: _____   Target met? _____

Target time: **8 minutes**

1. Complete these equivalent fractions.

a) $\frac{3}{5} = \frac{?}{25}$ _____

b) $\frac{4}{5} = \frac{24}{?}$ _____

c) $\frac{?}{4} = \frac{21}{28}$ _____

2. Find these amounts.

a) What is $\frac{7}{10}$ of £3.50? _____

b) What is $\frac{4}{5}$ of £12.20? _____

3. At a party, $\frac{1}{5}$ of the guests are men, $\frac{1}{3}$ are women, $\frac{2}{9}$ are girls and there are 44 boys.

How many men, women and girls are at the party?

a) Men _____

b) Women _____

c) Girls _____

4. Solve these calculations.

a) 202.6 + 20.6 + 2.06 = _____

b) 515 − 51.5 = _____

c) 0.09 × 8 = _____

d) 0.4 × _____ = 1.6

5. Convert 0.56 into a fraction and write the answer in its simplest form. _____

6. Convert $\frac{1}{8}$ into a percentage. _____

7. Write these fractions, decimals and percentages in ascending order.

$\frac{1}{5}$ 0.3   70%   0.45 $\frac{2}{3}$ 12%

_____

8. Harrison scored 90% in his maths test, having got 54 marks. What was the test out of? _____

9. A luggage shop sells suitcases for £210.

They buy them from the manufacturers for £175. What percentage profit are they making? _____

10. How many fifths are there in 9? _____

11. The angles in a triangle are in the ratio of 2:4:3.

a) What is the size of the largest angle? _____

b) What is the size of the smallest angle? _____

Score:	Time taken:	Target met?

1. If $a = 6$, $b = 9$ and $c = 13$, solve these equations.

a) $a^2 + b \times c =$ _____

b) $ac - 3a =$ _____

c) $3(bc) + 4a =$ _____

d) $(a + b)^2 - c =$ _____

2. Solve these equations.

a) $a + 5 = 1$ $a =$ _____

b) $\frac{a}{8} = 6$ $a =$ _____

3. Write a formula for each of these numbers. Use the example to help you.

> **Example** 20 plus a
> 20 + a

a) 5 less than x _____

b) y more than 7   _____

4. I think of a number, multiply it by 8 then subtract 14. The answer is 26.

a) What was my number?   _____

b) Write an algebraic equation to express this using n for number.   _____

5. Simplify these formulae.

a) $2a + 3a - a$ _____

b) $4b - 2b + 3b$ _____

6. Solve the equation $2n + 6 = 10$.

$n =$ _____

7. Use the equation to complete the table.

$y = 3x + 4$

x	y
4	
	10
9	

8. Multiply out the brackets.

a) $5(2a + 1) =$ _____

b) $3(4b + 7) =$ _____

9. Look at this triangle.

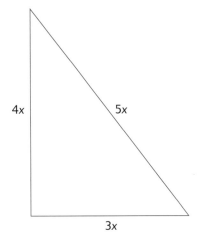

$4x$ $5x$

$3x$

a) Write the formula for the perimeter of the triangle, where P is the perimeter.   _____

b) If x is 7cm, calculate the perimeter of the triangle.   _____

Score: _____   **Time taken:** _____   **Target met?** _____

Target time: **8 minutes**

1. Imogen is practising for a local athletics competition. She times herself running and finds that she can run 100m in 12 seconds.

   a) What is that in metres per second? _____

   b) What is that in kilometres per hour? _____

2. Leona bought 6 hamburgers at £1.95 each. How much did she spend altogether? _____

3. A train travels 568km cross-country before returning along the same route. If the train does this same journey 4 times a day, how far does it travel each day? _____

4. The temperature one morning is −7°C. It drops by a further 5°C. What is the temperature now? _____

5. Convert these times.

12-hour clock	24-hour clock
9:34 a.m.	
	17:56
	22:13
11:27 p.m.	
	02:46

6. How many seconds are there in 2 hours and 12 minutes? _____

7. How many seconds are there in 3 hours and 23 minutes? _____

8. The perimeter of this rectangle is 97.6cm. What is its area?

   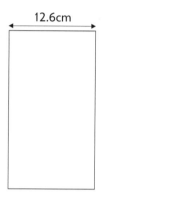

   14.6cm

   _____

9. The area of this rectangle is 316.26cm². What is its length?

   12.6cm

   _____

10. Finley buys a set of golf clubs for £376, a box of balls for £11.40 and a glove for £12.65. How much does he spend altogether? _____

11. Convert these measurements.

    a) 1.034l = _____ ml

    b) 5378kg = _____ tonnes

    c) 135mm = _____ m

    d) 1 pint ≈ _____ l

    (≈ means equals approximately)

12. A truck weighs 1458kg. It is about to cross a bridge that can withstand a weight of 1524kg. How much extra weight could the lorry afford to carry? _____

Score: _____ **Time taken:** _____ **Target met?** _____

Section 1 Test 5

1. **a)** Reflect the shape in the x axis and label it A.

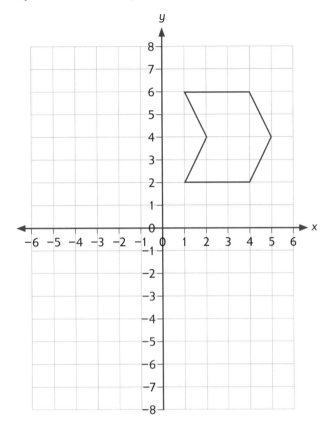

b) Rotate the original shape 90° anticlockwise about point (0, 2) and label it B.

c) Translate shape A L5 D1 and label it C.

d) What are the coordinates of shape C?

(_____ , _____)

(_____ , _____)

(_____ , _____)

(_____ , _____)

(_____ , _____)

(_____ , _____)

2. How many sides does a dodecagon have? _____

3. What is the name for a 7-sided polygon?

_____

4. Measure these angles.

a)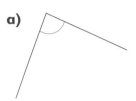
_____

b)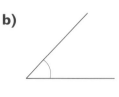
_____

c)
_____

d)
_____

e)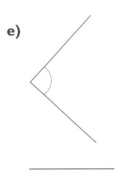
_____

f)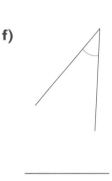
_____

5. Calculate the missing angles.

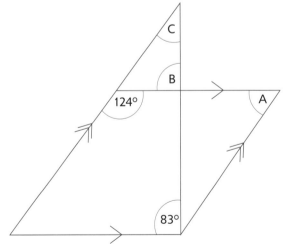

a) A = _____

b) B = _____

c) C = _____

Score: _____ Time taken: _____ Target met? _____

Target time: **8 minutes**

1. The line graph shows a cyclist's journey.

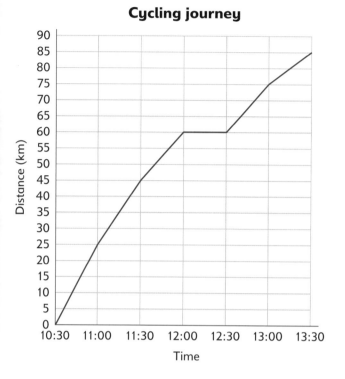

Cycling journey

a) How far had the cyclist
   travelled after 45 minutes? _____

b) What speed was he travelling
   between 10:30 and 11:00? _____

c) What speed was he travelling
   between 13:00 and 13:30? _____

d) At what time had he
   travelled 80km? _____

e) What happened between 12:00 and 12:30?

_____

f) What was the average speed
   of the entire journey? _____

2. Six students scored these marks on a test.

18, 15, 19, 21, 23, 18

a) What was the mean score? _____

b) What was the median score? _____

c) What was the modal score? _____

d) What was the range of
   scores? _____

3. Steve surveyed 120 children about their
   favourite crisp flavour. Measure the angles.

Favourite crisp flavours

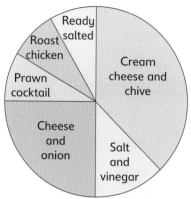

a) How many children chose
   cheese and onion? _____

b) How many children chose
   ready salted? _____

c) What fraction chose cream
   cheese and chive? _____

d) What percentage chose salt
   and vinegar? _____

e) How many more children
   liked salt and vinegar
   than prawn cocktail? _____

4. This chart shows the differences in times
   around the world compared to London.

Vancouver	New York	London	Manila	Sydney
−6 hr	−5 hr	0 hr	+7 hr	+10 hr

a) What is the time difference
   between Sydney and
   Vancouver? _____

b) If it is 14:15 in London,
   what time is it in Sydney? _____

c) If it is 09:13 in New York,
   what time is it in Manila? _____

d) If it is 22:37 in Vancouver,
   what time is it in London? _____

e) If it is 13:56 in Sydney, what
   time is it in New York? _____

Score: _____ Time taken: _____ Target met? _____

Target time: **8 minutes**

1. What is the value of the underlined digit?

a) 63 8<u>4</u>6 587 _____

b) 38 <u>6</u>77 035 _____

c) <u>1</u>25 783 657 _____

2. Write the largest prime number, square number and cube number under 30.

a) Prime number _____

b) Square number _____

c) Cube number _____

3. Salim is making a cake for his friend's birthday. It will take 42 minutes for the cake to bake.

a) If it goes into the oven at 15:37, at what time will it need to come out of the oven? _____

b) If the temperature of the oven is raised by 10°C, the cooking time can be reduced by 10%. How long will it take to bake now? _____

4. Convert $\frac{16}{25}$ into a decimal. _____

5. Convert $\frac{2}{5}$ into a percentage. _____

6. If $a = 7$, $b = 16$ and $c = 24$, solve these equations.

a) $ac + bc =$ _____

b) $c^2 - 3b - a =$ _____

c) $(c + a)^2 - 3b =$ _____

7. Selena earnt £7.50 an hour at her job. She worked 15.5 hours a week. How much did she earn in a year? _____

8. Lana's mother needs 14.6m of wool to knit a large rug. How much wool does she need to knit 15 large rugs? _____

9. Write the time difference between each pair of clocks.

a) _____

b) _____

c)

_____

d)

_____

10. Calculate the size of one of the interior angles of this regular polygon.

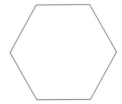

_____

Target time: **8 minutes**

1. Solve these calculations and write each remainder as a fraction.

a) $8 \overline{)1\ 8\ 4\ 7}$ _____

b) $1\ 1 \overline{)5\ 9\ 2\ 6}$ _____

2. When 8 649 567 is divided by 5, what is the remainder as a decimal? _____

3. Fifteen birthday cakes cost £368.25. What would six birthday cakes cost? _____

4. Write these fractions and decimals in ascending order.

$\frac{4}{5}$ 0.9 $\frac{2}{7}$ 0.44 $\frac{2}{3}$

_____

5. Write these numbers in ascending order.

1 345 893	5 936 023
945 023	
1 435 056	2 867 394

_____

_____

6. Write the formula to describe each sequence.

a) 7, 9, 11, 13, 15

nth term = _____

b) 1, 6, 11, 16, 21

nth term = _____

7. A shopkeeper wants to sell dishwashers for £325 but has to add on VAT (Value Added Tax) which is 20%. What price will he have to sell his dishwashers for? _____

8. The ratio of Freddie's age to Eddy's age is 3:5. Eddy is 10 years older than Freddie.

a) How old is Freddie? _____

b) How old is Eddy? _____

9. Damon had £137.67 in his bank account. Unfortunately, he had to have his car fixed which cost £153.95. What was the balance of his bank account after he paid for his car? _____

10. Solve these calculations and write each answer in its simplest form.

a) $\frac{4}{5} \div 2 =$ _____

b) $\frac{2}{5} \times \frac{4}{5} =$ _____

c) $\frac{5}{6} - \frac{2}{5} =$ _____

d) $\frac{2}{3} + \frac{4}{5} =$ _____

11. A train leaves the station at 13:16. It is travelling at 120km/hr.

a) How many kilometres has it travelled by 14:11? _____

b) How far has it travelled by 15:31? _____

c) It arrives after travelling 280km. What time does it arrive? _____

12. What is the probability of drawing an even-numbered red card from a pack of playing cards? Write the answer as a fraction in its simplest form. _____

Score:	Time taken:	Target met?

Target time: **8 minutes**

1. The following table shows Ali's runs in 5 cricket matches.

Match	1	2	3	4	5
Runs	22	13	15	21	19

   a) What was the mean number of runs per match? _____

   b) What was the median number of runs scored? _____

   c) If the mean number of runs over 6 matches was 20, what must Ali have scored in his 6th match? _____

2. Underline the prime numbers and circle the square numbers.

   1   3   4   7   9   12   15   19   25   27

3. Complete these sequences.

   a) 3, 5, 9, 17, 33, _____ , _____

   b) 1, 4, 9, 16, 25, _____ , _____

4. If a cake requires 450g of flour and 300g of sugar, how much sugar would be needed if a smaller cake was made with 300g of flour? _____

5. What is the name of the shape that this net creates?

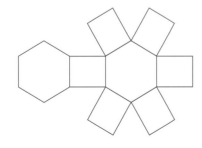

   _____

6. The following chart shows the climate of four cities in °C.

	Jan	Mar	May	Jul	Sep	Nov
Dubai	23.9	28.4	37.7	40.9	38.9	30.6
Anchorage	−11.4	−7.2	3.8	10.7	5.1	−8.4
London	6.8	8.8	14.8	19.6	17.3	10
Rome	7.2	10.4	18.5	25.4	21.1	12.5

   a) What is the difference between the hottest and coldest month across the four cities? _____

   b) What is the difference between the hottest and coldest May temperature? _____

   c) How much hotter is the temperature in London in July compared to November? _____

   d) How much warmer is the temperature in March in Rome compared to Anchorage? _____

7. If 1st March is a Tuesday, what day of the week will 12th April be? _____

8. $\frac{3}{8}$ of a number is 27. What is half of the number? _____

9. Solve these calculations.

   a) $38 \div 100 =$ _____

   b) $0.4 \times 100 =$ _____

   c) $7.6 \times 1000 =$ _____

   d) $2^4 =$ _____

   e) $10^5 =$ _____

Score:		Time taken:		Target met?	

Schofield & Sims

Target time: **8 minutes**

1. Solve these calculations.

   a) $6^2 \times 7 \div 9 + 4 \times 2 =$ _____

   b) $5736 \div 12 =$ _____

   c) $\boxed{?} + 56\,835\,835 = 89\,035\,247$

   _____

   d) $89\,341\,638 - \boxed{?} = 52\,849\,137$

   _____

2. 120 children were sitting an exam. Six of them had forgotten their pencil cases. What percentage had forgotten their pencil cases? _____

3. I think of a number, divide it by 7 then double it. The answer is 8.

   a) What was my number? _____

   b) Write an algebraic equation to express this using n for number. _____

4. The angles in a quadrilateral are in the ratio of 5:6:3:4.

   a) What is the size of the largest angle? _____

   b) What is the size of the smallest angle? _____

5. A plane is flying at 560 miles per hour. How many hours will it take the plane to travel 3500 miles? _____

6. What is the volume of this cuboid in cm³?

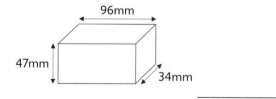

   96mm
   47mm
   34mm

   _____

7. Round these numbers to one decimal place.

   a) 3.24 _____

   b) 5.93 _____

8. A holiday company was charging £569.35 for each adult and £317.85 for each child. How much would a holiday cost for 2 adults and 3 children? _____

9. a) Reflect the triangle in the x axis and label it A.

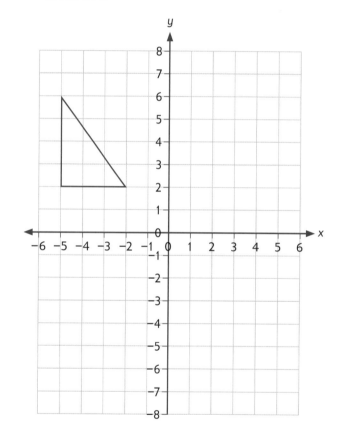

   b) Reflect triangle A in the y axis and label it B.

   c) Translate triangle B U6 L1. Label it C.

   d) What are the coordinates of triangle C?

   (_____ , _____)

   (_____ , _____)

   (_____ , _____)

Score: _____ **Time taken:** _____ **Target met?** _____

Target time: **8 minutes**

1. Write the correct operation signs and brackets to make these calculations correct.

   a) 2 _____ 6 _____ 8 = 20

   b) 3 _____ 7 _____ 2 = 5

   c) 5 _____ 7 _____ 2 = 45

2. $\frac{4}{5}$ of a number is 24. What is $\frac{1}{3}$ of the number? _____

3. Write these fractions, decimals and percentages in ascending order.

   $\frac{5}{7}$ 18%   0.65   81% $\frac{3}{4}$ 0.24

   _____

4. The mean age of 3 people is 22 years old. Their median is 20 and their range is 16. What are the ages of the 3 people?

   a) Youngest _____

   b) Middle _____

   c) Oldest _____

   d) What is the total age of all 3 people? _____

5. Each row and column in the grid below adds up to 42.

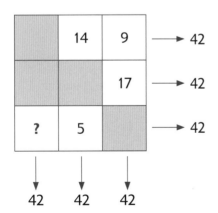

   What is the missing number? _____

6. A famous actor bought 4 houses around the country.

   Each house cost twice as much as the previous house. If the first house cost £355 000, what was the total cost of all four houses? _____

7. An easy way to convert between °C and °F is to use the following equation.

   °C × 1.8 + 32 = °F

   Use this equation to complete the table below.

°C		9	14		22
°F	23			64.4	

8. Jess measured the length of her garden using strides. She counted $47\frac{1}{2}$ strides.

   a) If each of her strides measures 76cm, how long is her garden in metres? _____

   b) She is going to put a fence on both sides of her garden at a cost of £38 per metre. How much is it going to cost her? _____

9. Solve the equation 4n − 3 = 13. _____

10. Solve the equation 2(n + 6) = 32. _____

Score: _____   Time taken: _____   Target met? _____

Target time: **8 minutes**

1. The number of ants in a colony doubles every 2 weeks. There are 145 ants in the colony at the beginning of the first fortnight.

   a) How many will there be after 8 weeks? _____

   b) After how many weeks will the colony pass 70 000? _____

2. Convert 5.6km into centimetres. _____

3. What is 348 × 99? _____

4. I go shopping with £27.50 in my purse. I come home with £11.85. How much have I spent? _____

5. How much smaller than $6\frac{1}{5}$ is $3\frac{4}{5}$? Write the answer as a decimal. _____

6. Alex and his team are installing street lights along a stretch of road. The road is 1.2km long. There needs to be a light at each end of the road and they have 16 lights to install in total. What will the spacing between each street light be in kilometres? _____

7. What is 3^3? _____

8. What is the value of the 6 digit in each of these numbers?

   a) 34 672 057 _____

   b) 56 035 712 _____

   c) 72 826 095 _____

   d) 62 809 553 _____

   e) 689 201 543 _____

9. Complete these equivalent fractions.

   a) $\frac{4}{7} = \frac{?}{35}$ _____

   b) $\frac{5}{6} = \frac{15}{?}$ _____

10. Convert 0.72 into a fraction and write the answer in its simplest form. _____

11. Gemma and her friends are going to the cinema. Tickets cost £9 but there is a 12% discount for every three tickets that are bought. If Gemma buys 7 tickets, how much will they cost altogether? _____

12. Write the formula to describe each sequence.

    a) 15, 20, 25, 30, 35

    nth term = _____

    b) 6, 7, 8, 9, 10

    nth term = _____

13. A zoo needs to transport three elephants.

The heaviest elephant weighs three times as much as the lightest elephant and the middle-sized elephant weighs half that of the heaviest elephant. If the lightest elephant weighs 2100kg, what is the total weight of the elephants? _____

Score:		Time taken:		Target met?	

Section 2 Test 1

1. What is the largest number less than 150 that can be made by multiplying 3 consecutive prime numbers? _____

2. Which multiple of 9 is closest to 500? _____

3. What is 5^3? _____

4. What is 3^4? _____

5. Solve these calculations.

   a) $22\,406\,428 + \boxed{?} = 67\,426\,046$

   _____

   b) $\boxed{?} - 34\,757\,901 = 21\,682\,924$

   _____

   c) $873 \times 83 =$ _____

   d) $1012 \div 22 =$ _____

   e) $7 + 13 \times 4 \div 2 =$ _____

   f) $56 - 3 \times 9 + 4^2 =$ _____

6. A hospital can cater for 5382 patients. It currently has 4805.

   After a busy evening, 263 more patients are admitted. How many more patients can the hospital now take? _____

7. Sammy has 52 174 building blocks. He drops the box and loses three hundred and eighty-nine blocks under the sofa. How many blocks does he still have? _____

8. $388 \times 124 = 48\,112$. Now solve these calculations.

   a) $388 \times 62 =$ _____

   b) $3.88 \times 124 =$ _____

   c) $38.8 \times 12.4 =$ _____

   d) $48\,112 \div 1.24 =$ _____

9. A printing factory can print 3415 books each hour.

   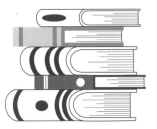

   It invests in a new machine that can increase productivity by 50%. How many books can the factory now print over a twelve-hour period? _____

10. Complete these function machines.

   a) _____ → $\boxed{\times 12}$ → $\boxed{-9}$ → 183

   b) _____ → $\boxed{\div 3}$ → $\boxed{\times 19}$ → 114

11. The population of a country is 5 463 198. If the population density is 18 people per km^2, what is the area of the country? _____

Score:		Time taken:		Target met?	

Target time: **8 minutes**

1. Each month Lara, Sam and Helen receive a sum of money. Sam receives three times as much as Helen, and Lara receives four times as much as Sam.

   a) What did Helen receive in April if Sam got £12? _____

   b) In September, Helen received £13. What did Lara receive? _____

In December, they received £240 altogether. What did they each receive?

   c) Lara _____

   d) Sam _____

   e) Helen _____

2. One third of Jyoti's friends have blond hair. $\frac{3}{5}$ have brown hair and the rest have black hair. Eight of her friends have black hair.

   a) How many have blond hair? _____

   b) How many have brown hair? _____

   c) How many friends does she have altogether? _____

3. There were 480 roses in a garden.

$\frac{2}{5}$ of the roses were red, $\frac{1}{3}$ were white and $\frac{1}{4}$ were pink. The rest were yellow. What fraction were yellow? Write the answer in its simplest form. _____

4. Convert $\frac{12}{40}$ into a percentage. _____

5. Ellie has a student card that allows her a 15% discount off clothes. She buys a T-shirt which cost £12.50, a pair of jeans which cost £31.80 and a skirt which cost £22.50 at their full prices. How much does she have to pay? _____

6. Solve these calculations.

   a) 1563 + 156.3 + 15.63 = _____

   b) 312 × 0.3 = _____

7. Write these fractions, decimals and percentages in descending order.

   12% $\frac{1}{8}$ 0.45 $\frac{3}{5}$ 0.74 75%

_____

8. Solve these calculations and write each answer in its simplest form.

   a) $2\frac{3}{4} + \frac{5}{6} =$ _____

   b) $\frac{3}{4} - \frac{7}{10} =$ _____

   c) $\frac{3}{5} \times \frac{5}{8} =$ _____

   d) $\frac{2}{9} \times \frac{4}{9} =$ _____

9. What is $\frac{5}{6}$ of 126? _____

10. There is 0.42kg of custard powder in a tin. A box contains 14 tins. What is the total mass of custard powder in the box, in grams? _____

Score:		Time taken:		Target met?	

Target time: **8 minutes**

1. Solve these equations.

a) $\frac{a}{14} = 4$ $a =$ _____

b) $3a + 7 = 43$ $a =$ _____

2. I think of a number, subtract 10 then multiply by 3. The answer is 12.

a) What was my number?   _____

b) Write an algebraic equation to express the calculation above, using n for number.   _____

3. Write a formula for each of these numbers.

Number	Formula
x more than 8	
6 times as big as b	
d divided by 7	

4. Simplify these formulae.

a) $5c + c - 4c$ _____

b) $4d \times 5d$ _____

5. Write the formula to describe each sequence.

a) $-8, -7, -6, -5, -4$

nth term = _____

b) $0, 2, 4, 6, 8$

nth term = _____

6. The pictures below show the patterns formed by joining regular pentagons.

Shape 1   Shape 2   Shape 3

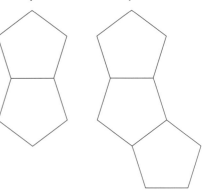

a) Complete the table to show the number of lines (L).

Shape number (S)	Number of lines (L)
1	5
2	9
3	
4	

b) What is the formula for L?   _____

c) How many lines would shape 20 have?   _____

d) What number shape would have 141 lines?   _____

7. The formula $a * b$ means $(a \times a) + (b \times b)$. Solve the following.

a) $4 * 2$ _____

b) $6 * 3$ _____

c) $b * 4 = 52$ $b =$ _____

d) $c * 7 = 130$ $c =$ _____

Score: _____   **Time taken:** _____   **Target met?** _____

Target time: **8 minutes**

1. Look at this menu for a café.

Café menu	
Soup	£1.20
Garlic bread	£2.15
Breaded mushrooms	£1.95
Caesar salad	£4.65
Fish & chips	£5.25
Vegetarian sausages & mash	£4.65
Chicken fajitas	£6.75
Ice cream	£2.85
Chocolate cake	£2.95
Fruit salad	£1.55

a) Jaya orders soup, fajitas and chocolate cake. How much is her bill? _____

b) If Jaya is given £1.10 change, how much did she give the waitress? _____

c) Lara and her sister order two garlic breads, a Caesar salad, vegetarian sausages and mash and two bowls of ice cream. What does their bill come to? _____

d) Harry orders breaded mushrooms, fish and chips, a fruit salad and some ice cream. How much does he end up paying? _____

e) What is Harry's change from a £20 note? _____

2. A rectangle has an area of 147cm². Its length is three times as long as its width.

a) How long is the rectangle? _____

b) How wide is the rectangle? _____

3. Debbie rode her bike for $2\frac{1}{2}$ hours. She covered a total of 36km. What was her average speed? _____

4. Raina went for a run at 09:34. She ran for 56 minutes, stopped for a drink for 12 minutes and then continued running for a further 37 minutes until she reached home. At what time did she get home? _____

5. Emma was born on 21st September 1995. Her sister, Sarah, was born on 21st June 1997. On 21st January 2014 how old were Emma and Sarah?

a) Emma _____

b) Sarah _____

6. At dawn, the thermometer in Susie's garden read −7°C. By lunchtime, the temperature had risen by 9°C. What was the temperature at lunchtime? _____

7. Convert these measurements.

a) 1.4 tonnes = _____ kg

b) 0.34km = _____ cm

c) 3l ≈ _____ pints

d) 3.5 days = _____ min

e) 12cm ≈ _____ inches

(≈ means equals approximately)

8. Billy weighs twice as much as his brother Oliver and half as much as his dad. In total, they weigh 164.5kg. What do each of them weigh?

a) Billy _____

b) Oliver _____

c) Dad _____

Score:		Time taken:		Target met?	

Target time: **8 minutes**

1. What is the total of the 6 labelled angles?

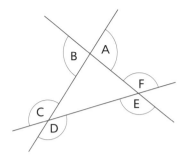

_____

2. **a)** Rotate the arrow 90° anticlockwise around point (−1, −2) and label the arrow A.

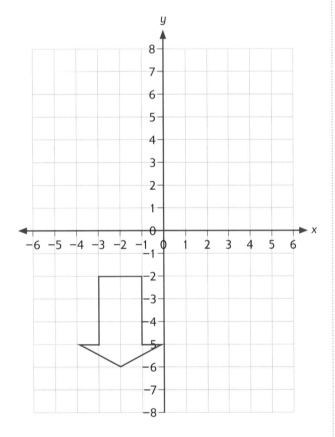

b) What are the coordinates of the rotated arrow's tip?

(_____, _____)

c) Reflect arrow A in the x axis and label it B.

d) What are the coordinates of the reflected arrow's tip?

(_____, _____)

3. Look at these words.

i. HANNAH   ii. MAM   iii. SHED

iv. TOOT   v. HIDE   vi. BOB

a) Which of these words are symmetrical? Write their numbers.

_____

b) Draw any lines of symmetry on the words.

4. Calculate the missing angles.

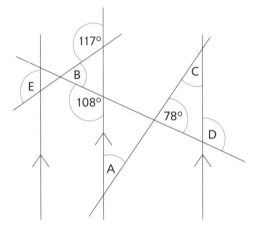

a) A = _____   **b)** B = _____

c) C = _____   **d)** D = _____

e) E = _____

5. What are the orders of rotational symmetry for these shapes?

a)

_____

b)

_____

Score: _____   **Time taken:** _____   **Target met?** _____

Notes for parents, tutors, teachers and other adult helpers

- **Maths Rapid Tests 6** is designed for 11- and 12-year-olds, but may also be suitable for some children of other ages.

- Remove this pull-out section before giving the book to the child.

- Before the child begins work on the first test, together read the instructions headed **What to do** on page 2. As you do so, point out to the child the suggested **Target time** for completing the test.

- Make sure the child has all the equipment in the list headed **What you need** on page 2. Also ensure that they are able to see a clock or a watch.

- There are three sections in this book. Each section consists of 12 tests. The first six tests focus on specific subject areas and the second six tests are a mix of these subject areas. Each mixed test will include questions from at least three of the subject areas. Details of the subject areas are given in the **Contents** page on page 3.

- Explain to the child how he or she should go about timing the test. Alternatively, you may wish to time the test yourself. When the child has finished the test, together work out the **Time taken** and complete the box that appears at the end of the test.

- Mark the child's work using this pull-out section. Each test is out of 20 marks and each individual question is worth one mark – this means that if a question is split into parts, each part will be worth one mark unless otherwise stated in the answers. All units of measure (for example, mm, cm, m, km, g and kg) should be included as part of the answer to qualify for the mark. Then complete the **Score** box at the end of the test.

- This table shows you how to mark the **Target met?** box and the **Action** notes help you to plan the next step. However, these are suggestions only. Please use your own judgement as you decide how best to proceed.

Score	Time taken	Target met?	Action
1–9	Any	Not yet	Give the child the previous book in the series. Provide help and support as needed.
10–13	Any	Not yet	Encourage the child to keep practising using the tests in this book. The child may need to repeat some tests. If so, wait a few weeks or the child may simply remember the correct answers. Provide help and support as needed.
14–20	Over target – child took too long	Not yet	
14–20	On target – child took suggested time or less	Yes	Encourage the child to keep practising using further tests in this book.

- After finishing each test, the child should fill in the **Progress chart** on page 40.

- Whatever the test score, always encourage the child to have another go at the questions that he or she got wrong – without looking at the answers. If the child's answers are still incorrect, work through these questions together. Demonstrate the correct method if necessary.

- If the child struggles with particular question types or mathematical areas, help him or her to develop the skills and strategies needed.

Answers

Unless otherwise stated, all fractions should be written in their simplest form.

Section 1 Test 1 (page 4)

1. a) 110 519 002

    b) 13 328 803

    c) 1632

    d) 23 115

    e) 105

2. 824 (2472 ÷ 3)

3. 9 years old (9 × 15 = 135. First, find the factor pairs for 135 and then find the pair with a difference of 6 between the factors.)

4. 77 (work backwards: 14 − 3 = 11, 11 × 7 = 77)

5. 24 (5 dozen = 5 × 12 = 60. 60 − 36 = 24.)

6. 1178 (1415 − 237)

7. 225 (1 + 8 + 27 + 64 + 125)

8. 15 (4710 ÷ 314)

9. a) 651

    b) $53\frac{13}{24}$ (the remaining 13 becomes the numerator and the divisor becomes the denominator)

10. a) + 3

    b) + 7

11. 60

12. 0.36

13. a) £1900 (14 × £50 = £700, £700 + £1200 = £1900)

    b) 25 (£2450 − £1200 = £1250. £1250 ÷ 50 = 25.)

Section 1 Test 2 (page 5)

1. a) 15 (To find an equivalent fraction, the numerator [top number] and denominator [bottom number] must be multiplied or divided by the same number. Here, both denominators are given but the numerator is missing in the second fraction. To find the missing number, do to the numerators what has been done to the denominators. So 5 × 5 = 25, 3 × 5 = 15.)

    b) 30 (4 has been multiplied by 6 to get 24 so to find the missing denominator you must multiply 5 by 6 = 30)

    c) 3 (4 has been multiplied by 7 to get 28 so to find the missing numerator you must divide 21 by 7 = 3)

2. a) £2.45 ($\frac{1}{10}$ of £3.50 = 35p, 35p × 7 = £2.45)

    b) £9.76 ($\frac{1}{5}$ of £12.20 = £2.44, £2.44 × 4 = £9.76)

3. a) 36 ($\frac{1}{5} + \frac{1}{3} + \frac{2}{9} = \frac{9}{45} + \frac{15}{45} + \frac{10}{45} = \frac{34}{45}$, so boys are $\frac{11}{45}$. If there are 44 boys, each $\frac{1}{45}$ is worth 4, so if men are $\frac{9}{45}$, 9 × 4 = 36.)

    b) 60 (women are $\frac{15}{45}$ so 15 × 4 = 60)

    c) 40 (girls are $\frac{10}{45}$ so 10 × 4 = 40)

4. a) 225.26

    b) 463.5

    c) 0.72

    d) 4

5. $\frac{14}{25}$ (0.56 = $\frac{56}{100} = \frac{28}{50} = \frac{14}{25}$)

6. 12.5% ($\frac{1}{8}$ = 0.125 = 12.5%)

7. 12% $\frac{1}{5}$ 0.3 0.45 $\frac{2}{3}$ 70% (convert them all into the same number type, e.g. percentages, so $\frac{1}{5}$ = 20%, 0.3 = 30%, 0.45 = 45%, $\frac{2}{3}$ = 66.6%)

8. 60 (if 54 is worth 90%, then 10% = 54 ÷ 9 = 6, so 100% = 6 × 10 = 60)

9. 20% (£210 − £175 = £35 profit. 10% of £175 = £17.50, so 20% = £35.)

10. 45 (9 × 5)

11. a) 80° (2:4:3 total 9. There are 180° in a triangle so 180° ÷ 9 = 20°, so each element of the ratio is worth 20°. The largest angle is 4 so 4 × 20° = 80°.)

    b) 40° (the smallest angle is 2 so 2 × 20° = 40°)

Section 1 Test 3 (page 6)

1. a) 153 (Use BODMAS. BODMAS tells you the order in which the operations should be done – **B**rackets, **O**rders [powers and square roots], **D**ivision, **M**ultiplication, **A**ddition, **S**ubtraction. So a^2 = 36, 9 × 13 = 117, so 36 + 117 = 153. BODMAS is sometimes also referred to as BIDMAS, where the 'I' stands for 'indices'.)

    b) 60 ($a × c$ = 78, $3a$ = 18, 78 − 18 = 60)

    c) 375 (bc = 117, 3 × 117 = 351, $4a$ = 24, 351 + 24 = 375)

    d) 212 ($a + b$ = 15, 15^2 = 225, 225 − 13 = 212)

2. a) −4

    b) 48

3. a) $x − 5$

    b) $7 + y$

4. a) 5 (work backwards: 26 + 14 = 40, 40 ÷ 8 = 5)

    b) $8n − 14 = 26$

5. a) 4a

  b) 5b

6. 2 (if 2n + 6 = 10, then 2n = 4, so n = 2)

7. (1 mark for each correct answer. Max. 3 marks.)

x	y
4	16
2	10
9	31

8. a) 10a + 5 (5 × 2a = 10a, 5 × 1 = 5)

  b) 12b + 21 (3 × 4b = 12b, 3 × 7 = 21)

9. a) P = 12x (5x + 3x + 4x)

  b) 84cm (12 × 7)

Section 1 Test 4 (page 7)

1. a) $8\frac{1}{3}$ m/sec (100m = 12 sec, 100 ÷ 12 = $8\frac{1}{3}$)

  b) 30km/hr (100m = 12 sec = 1000m = 120 sec
    [2 min], so if 1km = 2 min, then multiply by 30,
    so 30km = 60 min)

2. £11.70 (£1.95 × 6)

3. 4544km (568km × 2 = 1136km return journey.
    1136 × 4 = 4544km.)

4. −12°C (−7°C − 5°C)

5. (1 mark for each correct answer. Max. 5 marks.)

12-hour clock	24-hour clock
9:34 a.m.	09:34
5:56 p.m.	17:56
10:13 p.m.	22:13
11:27 p.m.	23:27
2:46 a.m.	02:46

6. 7920 sec (1 min = 60 sec, 60 min/1 hr = 3600 sec,
    2 hr = 7200 sec, 12 min = 720 sec, so 7200 sec +
    720 sec = 7920 sec)

7. 12 180 sec (1 hr = 3600 sec, 3 hr = 10 800 sec,
    23 min = 1380 sec, so 10 800 sec + 1380 sec =
    12 180 sec)

8. 499.32cm² (14.6cm + 14.6cm = 29.2cm, 97.6cm −
    29.2cm = 68.4cm, 68.4 ÷ 2 = 34.2cm so the length
    is 34.2cm. 34.2cm × 14.6cm = 499.32cm².)

9. 25.1cm (316.26 ÷ 12.6)

10. £400.05 (£376 + £11.40 + £12.65)

11. a) 1034ml

  b) 5.378 tonnes

  c) 0.135m

  d) $\frac{1}{2}$l

12. 66kg (1524kg − 1458kg)

Section 1 Test 5 (page 8)

1. a) (1 mark for a correct reflection)

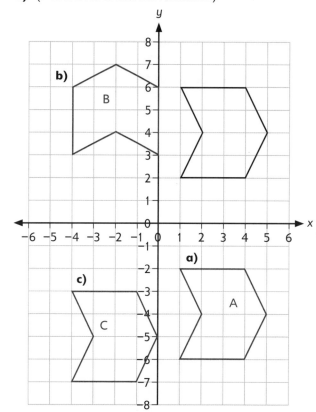

  b) (1 mark for a correct rotation. See grid above.)

  c) (1 mark for a correct translation. See grid above.)

  d) (−1, −7) (−4, −7) (−3, −5) (−4, −3) (−1, −3) (0, −5)
    in any order (1 mark for each correct coordinate.
    Max. 6 marks.)

2. 12

3. heptagon

4. a) 86° (allow +/−2°)

  b) 46° (allow +/−2°)

  c) 83° (allow +/−2°)

  d) 77° (allow +/−2°)

  e) 89° (allow +/−2°)

  f) 38° (allow +/−2°)

Answers

Section 1 Test 5 (page 8) continued

5. **a)** 56° (Additional letters have been added to the diagram below to aid with explanation. Y + Z = 124° as opposite angles in a parallelogram are equal, so Y must be 41°. X must be 83° as diagonally opposite angles where a line crosses a pair of parallel lines are equal (X and Z). Triangles have a total of 180° so A must be 56° as 83°+ 41°+ 56° = 180°.)

    b) 83° (X and B are opposite angles so B must be 83°)

    c) 41° (V must be 56° as angles on a straight line = 180° and 180° − 124° = 56°. C must therefore be 41° as the angles of a triangle = 180° and 83° + 56° + 41° = 180°.)

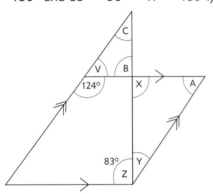

Section 1 Test 6 (page 9)

1. **a)** 35km

    b) 50km/hr (Speed is measured in kilometres or miles per hour, minute or second. To calculate speed, divide the distance covered by the time taken, e.g. if 25km is covered in half an hour, the calculation would be 25 ÷ 0.5 = 50km/hr.)

    c) 20km/hr

    d) 13:15

    e) he stopped

    f) $28\frac{1}{3}$km/hr (he travelled 85km in 3 hr)

2. **a)** 19 (18 + 15 + 19 + 21 + 23 + 18 = 114, 114 ÷ 6 = 19)

    b) 18.5 (The median is the middle value when the numbers are put in order: 15, 18, 18, 19, 21, 23. The middle number is halfway between 18 and 19 which is 18.5.)

    c) 18 (the most common number)

    d) 8 (the difference between the largest and smallest number, 23 − 15)

3. **a)** 30 ($\frac{1}{4}$ of the pie, 120 ÷ 4 = 30)

    b) 10 ($\frac{1}{12}$ of the pie, 120 ÷ 12 = 10)

    c) $\frac{3}{8}$ (the angle of this section measures 135° which is $\frac{3}{8}$ of 360°)

    d) 12.5% ($\frac{1}{8}$)

    e) 5 (15 liked salt and vinegar and 10 liked prawn cocktail)

4. **a)** 16 hr (6 hr to London time then another 10 hr to Sydney)

    b) 00:15 (14:15 + 10 hr)

    c) 21:13 (09:13 + 12 hr)

    d) 04:37 (22:37 + 6 hr)

    e) 22:56 (13:56 − 15 hr)

Section 1 Test 7 (page 10)

1. **a)** 3 000 000

    b) 600 000

    c) 100 000 000

2. **a)** 29

    b) 25

    c) 27

3. **a)** 16:19

    b) 37 min 48 sec (10% of 42 min = 4.2 min = 4 min 12 sec. 42 min − 4 min 12 sec = 37 min 48 sec.)

4. 0.64 ($\frac{16}{25} = \frac{64}{100}$)

5. 40% ($\frac{2}{5} = \frac{4}{10} = \frac{40}{100} = 40\%$)

6. **a)** 552 (168 + 384)

    b) 521 (576 − 48 − 7)

    c) 913 (961 − 48)

7. £6045 (£7.50 × 15.5 × 52)

8. 219m (14.6m × 15)

9. **a)** 1 hr 33 min

    b) 2 hr 29 min

    c) 6 hr 43 min

    d) 3 hr 43 min

10. 120° (6 triangles meet in the middle so each angle would be 60°. They would be equilateral triangles so the other 2 angles would equal 120° so 60° each. Each interior angle of the polygon would be made up of 2 of the triangle corners. 60° × 2 = 120°.)

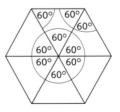

Section 1 Test 8 (page 11)

1. a) $230\frac{7}{8}$ (the remainder becomes the numerator and the divisor becomes the denominator)

    b) $538\frac{8}{11}$ (the remainder becomes the numerator and the divisor becomes the denominator)

2. 0.4 ($8\,649\,567 \div 5 = 1\,729\,913$ r.2. $\frac{2}{5} = 0.4$)

3. £147.30 (£368.25 $\div$ 15 = £24.55, £24.55 × 6 = £147.30)

4. $\frac{2}{7}$ 0.44 $\frac{2}{3}$ $\frac{4}{5}$ 0.9 (convert them all into the same number type, e.g. decimals, so $\frac{4}{5}$ = 0.8, $\frac{2}{7}$ is approximately 0.3, $\frac{2}{3}$ = 0.66)

5. 945 023   1 345 893   1 435 056   2 867 394   5 936 023

6. a) 2n + 5

    b) 5n − 4

7. £390 (10% of £325 = £32.50 so 20% = £65. £325 + £65 = £390.)

8. a) 15 (With a ratio of 3:5, Eddy would be 5 and Freddie would be 3, hence a difference of only 2 years. To make it 10 years, multiply both parts of the ratio by 5, so 3:5 = 15:25.)

    b) 25

9. −£16.28 (£137.67 − £153.95)

10. a) $\frac{2}{5}$

    b) $\frac{8}{25}$ (multiply the numerators and multiply the denominators)

    c) $\frac{13}{30}$ ($\frac{5}{6} = \frac{25}{30}$, $\frac{2}{5} = \frac{12}{30}$, so $\frac{25}{30} - \frac{12}{30} = \frac{13}{30}$)

    d) $1\frac{7}{15}$ ($\frac{2}{3} = \frac{10}{15}$, $\frac{4}{5} = \frac{12}{15}$, so $\frac{10}{15} + \frac{12}{15} = \frac{22}{15}$. $\frac{22}{15} = 1\frac{7}{15}$.)

11. a) 110km (120km/hr = 20km/10 min = 10km/5min. The train has travelled for 55 min = 110km.)

    b) 270km (the train has travelled for 2 hr 15 min = 270km)

    c) 15:36 (If 10km = 5 min, 280km $\div$ 10 = 28, so 28 × 5 = 140 min = 2 hr 20 min. 13:16 + 2 hr 20 min = 15:36.)

12. $\frac{5}{26}$ (There are 5 even-numbered cards in each suit [2, 4, 6, 8 and 10] and there are 2 red suits [diamonds and hearts]. Out of a total of 52 cards, 10 will be even and red. $\frac{10}{52} = \frac{5}{26}$.)

Section 1 Test 9 (page 12)

1. a) 18 (22 + 13 + 15 + 21 + 19 = 90, 90 $\div$ 5 = 18)

    b) 19 (the median is the middle value when the numbers are put in order: 13, 15, 19, 21, 22)

    c) 30 (If the mean was 20, the total over 6 matches would be 120. The previous total was 90, so 120 − 90 = 30.)

2. (1 mark for all correct prime numbers. 1 mark for all correct square numbers. Max. 2 marks.)
    (1) 3 4 7 (9) 12 15 19 (25) 27

3. a) 65, 129 (add double the difference each time)

    b) 36, 49 (square numbers)

4. 200g ($\frac{2}{3}$ of the flour is being used, so $\frac{2}{3}$ of the sugar is needed)

5. hexagonal prism

6. a) 52.3°C (40.9°C − −11.4°C)

    b) 33.9°C (37.7°C − 3.8°C)

    c) 9.6°C (19.6°C − 10°C)

    d) 17.6°C (10.4°C − −7.2°C)

7. Tuesday (March has 31 days)

8. 36 (If $\frac{3}{8}$ = 27, $\frac{1}{8}$ = 9 so the number is 72. 72 $\div$ 2 = 36.)

9. a) 0.38

    b) 40

    c) 7600

    d) 16 (2 × 2 × 2 × 2 = 16)

    e) 100 000 (10 × 10 × 10 × 10 × 10 = 100 000)

Section 1 Test 10 (page 13)

1. a) 36 (BODMAS applies so 36 × 7 = 252, 252 $\div$ 9 = 28, 4 × 2 = 8, 28 + 8 = 36. BODMAS is explained on page A2, Section 1, Test 3, q1a).)

    b) 478

    c) 32 199 412

    d) 36 492 501

2. 5% ($\frac{6}{120} = \frac{1}{20}$ = 5%)

3. a) 28 (work backwards: 8 $\div$ 2 = 4, 4 × 7 = 28)

    b) $2(\frac{n}{7}) = 8$

4. a) 120° (The ratio 5:6:3:4 totals 18. There are 360° in a quadrilateral so 360° $\div$ 18 = 20°. Each part of the ratio is worth 20° so 20 × 6 = 120°.)

    b) 60° (20 × 3 = 60°)

Answers

Section 1 Test 10 (page 13) continued

5. $6\frac{1}{4}$ hr ($3500 \div 560 = 6\frac{1}{4}$)

6. 153.408cm³ (convert the measurements to cm first, so 4.7cm × 9.6cm × 3.4cm)

7. **a)** 3.2 (when the hundredths are 4 or less, the number is rounded down to the existing tenth)

    b) 5.9 (when the hundredths are 4 or less, the number is rounded down to the existing tenth)

8. £2092.25 (£569.35 × 2 = £1138.70, £317.85 × 3 = £953.55, so £1138.70 + £953.55 = £2092.25)

9. **a)** (1 mark for a correct reflection)

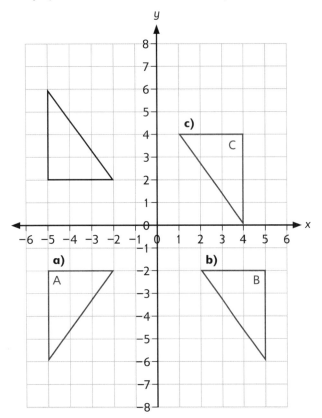

    b) (1 mark for a correct reflection. See grid above.)

    c) (1 mark for a correct translation. See grid above.)

    d) (4, 0) (4, 4) (1, 4) in any order (1 mark for each correct coordinate. Max. 3 marks.)

Section 1 Test 11 (page 14)

1. **a)** 2 × 6 + 8

    b) (3 + 7) ÷ 2

    c) 5 × (7 + 2)

2. 10 (If $\frac{4}{5}$ = 24, then $\frac{1}{5}$ = 6, so the whole is 30. $\frac{1}{3}$ of 30 = 10.)

3. 18% 0.24 0.65 $\frac{5}{7}$ $\frac{3}{4}$ 81% (convert them all into the same number type, e.g. percentages, so $\frac{5}{7}$ is approximately 71%, 0.65 = 65%, $\frac{3}{4}$ = 75%, 0.24 = 24%)

4. **a)** 15 (If the mean is 22 then the total is 66. If the median is 20, then the oldest and youngest ages = 46. If their range is 16 years then one must be 31 and one must be 15.)

    b) 20

    c) 31

    d) 66

5. 21

6. 5 325 000 (£355 000 + £710 000 + £1 420 000 + £2 840 000)

7. (1 mark for each correct answer. Max. 5 marks.)

°C	−5	9	14	18	22
°F	23	48.2	57.2	64.4	71.6

8. **a)** 36.1m (47.5 × 76cm = 3610cm = 36.1m)

    b) £2743.60 (36.1 × £38 = £1371.80, £1371.80 × 2 = £2743.60)

9. 4

10. 10

Section 1 Test 12 (page 15)

1. **a)** 2320 (at the end of the 2nd week there would be 290, end of 4th = 580, end of 6th = 1160, end of 8th 2320)

    b) 18 (at the end of 18th week there would be 74 240)

2. 560 000cm (5.6km = 5600m = 560 000cm)

3. 34 452 (348 × 100 = 34 800, 34 800 − 348 = 34 452)

4. £15.65 (£27.50 − £11.85)

5. 2.4 (6.2 − 3.8)

6. 0.08km (16 lights will have 15 spaces between them. 1.2km ÷ 15 = 0.08km.)

7. 27 (3 × 3 × 3)

8. **a)** 600 000

    b) 6 000 000

    c) 6000

    d) 60 000 000

    e) 600 000 000

9. a) 20 (7 has been multiplied by 5 to get 35 so 4 × 5 = 20)

b) 18 (5 has been multiplied by 3 to get 15 so 6 × 3 = 18)

10. $\frac{18}{25}$ (0.72 = $\frac{72}{100}$ = $\frac{36}{50}$ = $\frac{18}{25}$)

11. £56.52 (10% of £9 = 90p, 1% of £9 = 9p so 12% of £9 = £1.08. 3 full price tickets would cost £9 × 3 = £27 but with the discount would be £7.92 × 3 = £23.76. She can buy 2 sets of 3 tickets with the discount, so £23.76 × 2 = £47.52, plus 1 full price ticket at £9 = £56.52.)

12. a) $5n + 10$

b) $n + 5$

13. 11 550kg (The lightest is 2100kg, so the heaviest is 2100kg × 3 = 6300kg, so the middle elephant weighs 6300kg ÷ 2 = 3150kg. 2100kg + 6300kg + 3150kg = 11 550kg.)

Section 2 Test 1 (page 16)

1. 105 (3 × 5 × 7)

2. 504 (The digits of a number that is a multiple of 9 will always add up to 9 or a multiple of 9. 5 + 0 + 4 = 9.)

3. 125 (5 × 5 × 5)

4. 81 (3 × 3 × 3 × 3)

5. a) 45 019 618

b) 56 440 825

c) 72 459

d) 46

e) 33 (BODMAS applies so 13 × 4 = 52, 52 ÷ 2 = 26, 7 + 26 = 33. BODMAS is explained on page A2, Section 1, Test 3, q1a).)

f) 45 (BODMAS applies so 4^2 = 16, 3 × 9 = 27, 56 − 27 = 29, 29 + 16 = 45. BODMAS is explained on page A2, Section 1, Test 3, q1a).)

6. 314 (5382 − 4805 = 577, 577 − 263 = 314)

7. 51 785 (52 174 − 389)

8. a) 24 056 (62 is half 124 so the answer is half)

b) 481.12 (388 has been made 100× smaller so the answer is 100× smaller)

c) 481.12 (as both numbers have been made 10× smaller the answer needs to be 100× smaller)

d) 38 800 (this is the inverse calculation with one number being 100× smaller so the answer needs to be 100× bigger)

9. 61 470 (50% of 3415 = 1707.5, 3415 + 1707.5 = 5122.5, 5122.5 × 12 = 61 470)

10. a) 16 (work backwards: 183 + 9 = 192, 192 ÷ 12 = 16)

b) 18 (work backwards: 114 ÷ 19 = 6, 6 × 3 = 18)

11. 303 511km² (5 463 198 ÷ 18)

Section 2 Test 2 (page 17)

1. a) £4 (£12 ÷ 3 = £4)

b) £156 (if Helen receives £13, Sam receives £39, so Lara receives £39 × 4 = £156)

c) £180 (The ratio of the money is 12:3:1 for Lara, Sam and Helen. That totals 16. £240 ÷ 16 = £15, 12 × £15 = £180.)

d) £45 (3 × £15)

e) £15 (1 × £15)

2. a) 40 ($\frac{1}{3}$ + $\frac{3}{5}$ = $\frac{5}{15}$ + $\frac{9}{15}$ = $\frac{14}{15}$, so $\frac{1}{15}$ have black hair. If 8 = $\frac{1}{15}$, then the total number of friends is 120. $\frac{1}{3}$ of 120 = 40.)

b) 72 ($\frac{3}{5}$ of 120 = 72)

c) 120

3. $\frac{1}{60}$ (192 were red, 160 were white and 120 were pink, leaving 8 yellow roses. $\frac{8}{480}$ in its simplest form is $\frac{1}{60}$.)

4. 30% ($\frac{12}{40}$ = $\frac{3}{10}$ = 30%)

5. £56.78 (£12.50 + £31.80 + £22.50 = £66.80. 10% of £66.80 = £6.68, 5% of £66.80 = £3.34 so 15% = £10.02. £66.80 − £10.02 = £56.78.)

6. a) 1734.93

b) 93.6

7. 75%   0.74 $\frac{3}{5}$ 0.45 $\frac{1}{8}$ 12% (convert all to the same number type, e.g. percentages, so $\frac{1}{8}$ = 12.5%, 0.45 = 45%, $\frac{3}{5}$ = 60%, 0.74 = 74%)

8. a) $3\frac{7}{12}$ ($2\frac{3}{4}$ = $\frac{33}{12}$, $\frac{5}{6}$ = $\frac{10}{12}$, so 33 + 10 = $\frac{43}{12}$ = $3\frac{7}{12}$)

b) $\frac{1}{20}$ ($\frac{3}{4}$ = $\frac{15}{20}$, $\frac{7}{10}$ = $\frac{14}{20}$, so $\frac{15}{20}$ − $\frac{14}{20}$ = $\frac{1}{20}$)

c) $\frac{3}{8}$ (multiply the numerators then multiply the denominators so $\frac{3}{5}$ × $\frac{5}{8}$ = $\frac{15}{40}$ = $\frac{3}{8}$)

d) $\frac{8}{81}$ (multiply the numerators then multiply the denominators)

9. 105 ($\frac{1}{6}$ of 126 = 21, so $\frac{5}{6}$ = 105)

10. 5880g (0.42kg = 420g, 420g × 14 = 5880g)

Answers

Section 2 Test 3 (page 18)

1. **a)** 56 (work backwards: 14 × 4 = 56)
   b) 12
2. **a)** 14 (work backwards: 12 ÷ 3 = 4, 4 + 10 = 14)
   b) 3(n − 10) = 12
3. (1 mark for each correct answer. Max. 3 marks.)

Number	Formula
x more than 8	8 + x
6 times as big as b	6b
d divided by 7	$\frac{d}{7}$

4. **a)** 2c
   b) 20d²
5. **a)** n − 9
   b) 2n − 2
6. **a)** (1 mark for each correct answer. Max. 2 marks.)

Shape number (S)	Number of lines (L)
1	5
2	9
3	13
4	17

   b) 4S + 1
   c) 81 (4 × 20 = 80, 80 + 1 = 81)
   d) 35 (4S + 1 = 141, so 4S = 140 so S = 35)
7. **a)** 20 (4 × 4 + 2 × 2)
   b) 45 (6 × 6 + 3 × 3)
   c) 6 (4 × 4 = 16, 52 − 16 = 36, 6 × 6 = 36)
   d) 9 (7 × 7 = 49, 130 − 49 = 81, 9 × 9 = 81)

Section 2 Test 4 (page 19)

1. **a)** £10.90 (£1.20 + £6.75 + £2.95)
   b) £12 (£10.90 + £1.10)
   c) £19.30 (£2.15 + £2.15 + £4.65 + £4.65 + £2.85 + £2.85)
   d) £11.60 (£1.95 + £5.25 + £1.55 + £2.85)
   e) £8.40 (£20 − £11.60)
2. **a)** 21cm (first, find the factor pairs for 147 and then find the pair where one factor is 3 times bigger than the other)
   b) 7cm

3. 14.4km/hr (36 ÷ 2.5. This can be done by scaling, e.g. 360 ÷ 25 = 14.4. See page A4, Section 1, Test 6, q1b).)
4. 11:19 (9:34 + 56 min = 10:30, 10:30 + 12 min = 10:42, 10:42 + 37 min = 11:19)
5. **a)** 18 (on 21st September 2013 she would turn 18, so would still be 18 in January 2014)
   b) 16 (on 21st June 2013 she would turn 16, so would still be 16 in January 2014)
6. 2°C (−7°C + 9°C)
7. **a)** 1400kg
   b) 34000cm
   c) 6 pints
   d) 5040 min
   e) 5 inches
8. **a)** 47kg (The ratio would be 2:1:4 for Billy:Oliver:Dad. That totals 7. 164.5kg ÷ 7 = 23.5kg, so 23.5kg × 2 = 47kg.)
   b) 23.5kg (23.5kg × 1)
   c) 94kg (23.5kg × 4)

Section 2 Test 5 (page 20)

1. 720° (The angles within the triangle would equal 180° as would their opposites, so totalling 360°. A circle is 360° so each cross measures 360° which totals 1080°. 1080° − 360° = 720°.)
2. **a)** (1 mark for a correct rotation)

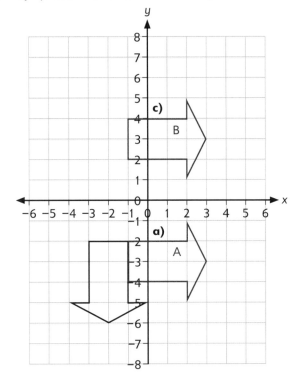

b) (3, −3)

c) (1 mark for a correct reflection. See grid on previous page.)

d) (3, 3)

3. a) ii, iv, v, vi (1 mark for each correct answer. Max. 4 marks.)

b) (1 mark for each correct answer. Max. 4 marks.)

i. HANNAH   ii. MAM   iii. SHED

iv. TOOT   v. ~~HIDE~~   vi. ~~BOB~~

4. a) 30° (Additional letters have been added to the diagram below to aid with explanation. The other 2 angles in the triangle are 72° as 108° + 72° = 180°, and 78° as opposite angles are equal. 72° + 78° = 150°, 180° − 150° = 30°.)

b) 45° (The other 2 angles in the triangle are 63° as 117° + 63° = 180°, and 72° as 108° + 72° = 180°. 63° + 72° = 135°, 180° − 135° = 45°.)

c) 30° (C is the same as A as opposite angles made by a line bisecting a pair of parallel lines are equal)

d) 108° (If C is 30° and the other angle in the triangle is 78°, then Z must be 72° as 78° + 30° = 108° and 180° − 108° = 72°. D must therefore be 108° as a straight line is 180° and 72° + 108° = 180°.)

e) 117° (opposite angles where a line bisects a pair of parallel lines are equal [X and Y] and opposite angles where 2 lines cross are equal [X and E] so E must be 117°)

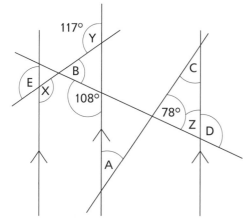

5. a) 2 (it will look exactly the same on 2 occasions if it is rotated 360°)

b) 4 (it will look exactly the same on 4 occasions if it is rotated 360°)

Section 2 Test 6 (page 21)

1. a) (see Venn diagram below)

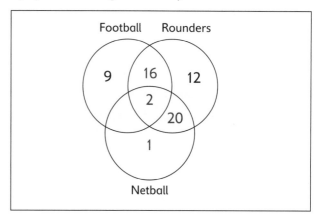

b) (see Venn diagram above)

c) (see Venn diagram above)

d) (see Venn diagram above)

e) 16 (9 + 16 + 12 + 2 + 20 + 1 = 60, 76 − 60 = 16)

2. a)

b)

c)

d)

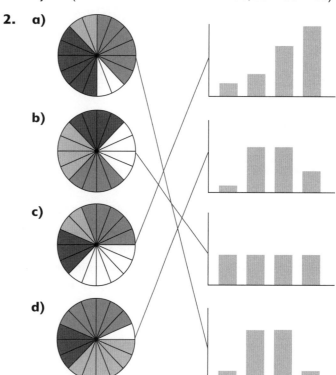

3. a) 9km

b) 45 min (10:30–11:15)

c) 12km/hr (9km in 45 min = 3km in 15 min = 12km in 60 min)

d) 45 min (the flat line at the top where he did not travel anywhere)

e) 30 min (12:00–12:30)

f) 18km/hr (9km in 30 min = 18km in 60 min)

Answers

Section 2 Test 6 (page 21) continued

4. (1 mark for each correct answer. Max. 5 marks. If the average over 6 games is 36, the total has to be 216. Game 2: 2 × 18 = 36, Game 3: 2.5 × 18 = 45, Games 4, 5 and 6: 18 + 36 + 45 = 99. 216 − 99 = 117. 117 ÷ 3 = 39.)

Game 1	Game 2	Game 3	Game 4	Game 5	Game 6
18	36	45	39	39	39

Section 2 Test 7 (page 22)

1. a) 35% (if 364 are women, 196 are men, $\frac{196}{560}$ = $\frac{7}{20}$ = 0.35 = 35%)

   b) £19 600 (£35 × 560)

2. a) 55 (10 × 11 = 110, 110 ÷ 2 = 55)

   b) 5050 (100 × 101 = 10 100, 10 100 ÷ 2 = 5050)

3. 414 miles (2 hr = 126 miles, 20 min = 21 miles, 126 + 21 = 147 miles, so 147 + 267 = 414 miles)

4. (1 mark for all correct square numbers. 1 mark for all correct cube numbers. Max. 2 marks.)

   ① 4̲ ⑧ 1̲6̲   2̲5̲   37   ㉔   91

5. 336 hr (24 × 14)

6. 600 hr (24 × 25)

7. 1461 days (365 days in a normal year and 366 in a leap year. There will be 1 leap year in 4 consecutive years, so 365 × 3 = 1095, 1095 + 366 = 1461.)

8. 86 400 sec (1 day = 24 hr = 1440 min = 86 400 sec)

9. 6cm (Split the compound shape into 2 rectangles. The top rectangle has measurements of 17cm × 8cm so the area is 17cm × 8cm = 136cm². If the total area is 154cm², then 154cm² − 136cm² = 18cm² so the bottom rectangle has an area of 18cm². The bottom rectangle has one measurement of 3cm so the other must be 6cm as 3cm × 6cm = 18cm².)

10. 36

11. 12

12. 801 (The digits of a number that is a multiple of 3 will always add up to 3, 6 or 9. 8 + 0 + 1 = 9.)

13. 295 (456 − 134 = 322, 322 ÷ 2 = 161, 134 + 161 = 295)

14. a) $1\frac{2}{9}$ ($\frac{2}{3}$ = $\frac{6}{9}$, so $\frac{5}{9}$ + $\frac{6}{9}$ = $\frac{11}{9}$ = $1\frac{2}{9}$)

    b) $\frac{7}{36}$ ($\frac{1}{12}$ ÷ 3 = $\frac{1}{36}$, so $\frac{7}{12}$ ÷ 3 = $\frac{7}{36}$)

c) $\frac{3}{14}$ (multiply the numerator, then multiply the denominator and simplify)

d) $\frac{1}{3}$ ($\frac{1}{2}$ = $\frac{3}{6}$, so $\frac{3}{6}$ − $\frac{1}{6}$ = $\frac{2}{6}$ = $\frac{1}{3}$)

Section 2 Test 8 (page 23)

1. a) 7 (A rabbit and a horse total 30° so 15° each. 15° is $\frac{1}{24}$ of the pie chart. $\frac{1}{24}$ of 168 = 7.)

   b) 42 (A dog is $\frac{1}{4}$ of the pie chart. 168 ÷ 4 = 42.)

   c) 12.5% (A dolphin and a lion are equal and together make 90° so are 45° each. That is $\frac{1}{8}$ of the pie chart. $\frac{1}{8}$ = 12.5%.)

   d) $\frac{1}{12}$ (a cat makes up 30° of the pie chart which is $\frac{1}{12}$ of 360°)

   e) 28 (An elephant is 60° which is $\frac{1}{6}$ of the pie chart. 168 ÷ 6 = 28.)

2. a) 30m (The room is 2.5m wide and the planks are 0.25m wide, so the room is 10 planks wide. As the room is 3m long, 3m × 10 = 30m.)

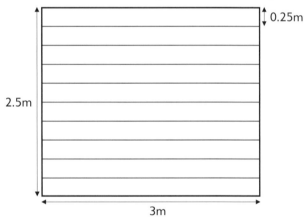

   b) 25 (each plank is 1.2m long, so 30m ÷ 1.2m = 25)

3. a) 216, 343 (cubed numbers)

   b) 35, 47 (add an extra 2 each time)

4. a) 173.02 (when the thousandths are 5 or more, the number is rounded up to the next hundredth)

   b) 35.95 (when the thousandths are 5 or more, the number is rounded up to the next hundredth)

   c) 69.38 (when the thousandths are 5 or more, the number is rounded up to the next hundredth)

   d) 437.82 (when the thousandths are 4 or less, the number is rounded down to the existing hundredth)

5. a) 6.3m² (4.2m × 1.5m)

   b) 49.37m² (The veg patch is 6.3m², the flower bed is 3.8m² × 1.1m² = 4.18m², 6.3m² + 4.18m² = 10.48m². The entire garden is 6.3m × 9.5m = 59.85m² so 59.85m² − 10.48m² = 49.37m².)

c) 21.2m (flower bed = 3.8m + 3.8m + 1.1m + 1.1m = 9.8m, veg patch = 4.2m + 4.2m + 1.5m + 1.5m = 11.4m, so 9.8m + 11.4m = 21.2m)

d) £69.30 (The edging is sold per metre so Joe will have to buy 22 metres. £3.15 × 22 = £69.30.)

6. a) 7 × 3 + 4 − 9 = 16

b) 16 ÷ 4 × 8 + 6 = 38

7. 343 (7 × 7 × 7)

Section 2 Test 9 (page 24)

1. a) 52 (The ratio of mother:daughter:son:son is 4:2:1:1 which totals 8. 104 ÷ 8 = 13 so 4 × 13 = 52.)

b) 26 (2 × 13 = 26)

c) 13 (1 × 13 = 13)

2. £6706.50 (10% of £7890 = £789, 5% of £7890 = £394.50, so 15% of £7890 = £1183.50. £7890 − £1183.50 = £6706.50.)

3. 858km (1456km − 598km = 858km)

4. £106.08 (He worked 105 min a day × 6 days = 630 min = $10\frac{1}{2}$hr. $10\frac{1}{2}$ × £4.48 = £47.04. 123 × 8p = £9.84, £9.84 × 6 days = £59.04. £47.04 + £59.04 = £106.08.)

5. a) 1 hr 47 min

b) 5 hr 49 min

6. 165cm² (Split the parallelogram into 2 triangles and a rectangle. The triangles are 11cm × 4cm = 44cm², 44cm² ÷ 2 = 22cm² each. The rectangle measures 11cm × 11cm = 121cm². 121cm² + 22cm² + 22cm² = 165cm².)

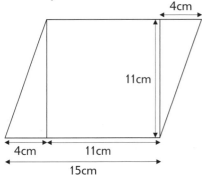

7. a) 6a + 12b

b) 12a + 8b

8. a) 2

b) 3

9. a) 7826.1

b) 94

10. a) 1331 (If the ones digit is increased by 1, the thousands digit will also have to increase by 1, which will increase the size of the number too quickly. Therefore, the tens digit should increase by 1, which means the hundreds digit will also increase by 1.)

b) 13531

c) 855 (151 + 161 + 171 + 181 + 191)

11. a) 70 000 000

b) 2 000 000

Section 2 Test 10 (page 25)

1. (1 mark for each correct answer. Max. 3 marks.)

x	7	12	3
y	22	42	6

2. 15

3. a) £279.50 (10% of £215 = £21.50 so 30% = £64.50, £215 + £64.50 = £279.50)

b) £967.50 (15 × £215 = £3225, 15 × £279.50 = £4192.50, so £4192.50 − £3225 = £967.50)

4. a) £2.67 (10% of £8.90 = 89p so 30% = £2.67)

b) £2.52 (10% of £5.60 = 56p, so 5% of £5.60 = 28p, 40% = £2.24, so £2.24 + 28p = £2.52)

c) £4.03 (10% of £6.50 = 65p, so 1% = 6.5p, 60% = £3.90, 2% = 13p, so 62% = £4.03)

5. a) 7 × 3

b) 5 × 3 × 3

c) 3 × 2 × 2

6. 420cm³ (find the volume of the cuboid then halve so 15cm × 8cm × 7cm = 840cm³, 840cm³ ÷ 2 = 420cm³)

7. a) 39 min (08:56 to 09:35)

b) B

c) C (38 min)

d) 09:50 (the 09:24 should arrive at 09:43 but is 7 min late)

8. a) 450g (Double the first set so the apples are the same, so 4 bags of flour and 6 apples = 2220g and 3 bags of flour and 6 apples = 1770g. The difference is 1 bag of flour and 450g so 1 bag of flour = 450g. So 3 bags of flour = 1350g, 1770g − 1350g = 420g, so 6 apples = 420g, so 1 apple = 70g.)

b) 70g

9. 8 ($\frac{1}{3}$ of 48 = 16, $\frac{1}{2}$ of 16 = 8)

Answers

Section 2 Test 11 (page 26)

1. **a)** £23 010.05 (10% of £22 670 = £2267, so 1% = £226.70 and 0.5% = £113.35 so 1.5% = £340.05. £22 670 + £340.05 = £23 010.05.)

   b) £18 408.04 (10% of £23 010.05 = £2301.005, so 20% = £4602.01. £23 010.05 − £4602.01 = £18 408.04.)

   c) £1534 (£18 408.04 ÷ 12 = £1534.00333 so £1534 to the nearest pound)

2. 12.2 12.1 12.01 2.12 1.21 (To order easily, all decimals need the same number of digits after the decimal point. 12.1 and 12.2 only have 1 digit after the decimal while all the others have 2 digits so you need to put a zero on the end, e.g. 12.10. This does not change the value of the numbers. Now imagine the decimals are 3- and 4-digit whole numbers, e.g. 1210, 121, 212, 1201, 1220. Now put them in order.)

3. **a)** 100

   b) 1000

4. n^2

5. tetrahedron

6. £550 800 (10% of £540 000 = £54 000, so 1% = £5400 so 2% = £10 800. £540 000 + £10 800 = £550 800.)

7. **a)** 52° (Additional letters have been added to the diagram below to aid with explanation. A must be 52° as when a line bisects a pair of parallel lines, the opposite angles are equal.)

   b) 61° (X must be 67° as 180° − 113° = 67°. As A = 52°, 52° + 67° = 119°, so Y must be 180° − 119° = 61°. B must therefore be 61° as opposite angles are equal.)

   c) 67° (If B = 61°, 61° + 52° = 113°. A straight line is 180° so C must be 180° − 113° = 67°.)

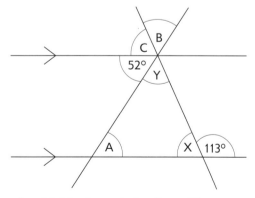

8. **a)** −30 (the formula is −7n + 19)

   b) −331 (the formula is −7n + 19)

9. (1 mark for each correct answer. Max. 6 marks.)

Fraction	Decimal	Percentage
$\frac{9}{30}$	0.3	30%
$\frac{1}{8}$	0.125	12.5%
$\frac{37}{50}$	0.74	74%

Section 2 Test 12 (page 27)

1. (1 mark for each correctly filled section. Max. 4 marks.)

	Odd	Not odd
Prime	3 5 7	2
Not prime	1 9	4 6 8 10

2. **a)** $25e^2$

   b) $17a$

3. **a)** £18.13 (£36 + £27 + £52.20 + £14.30 = £129.50. 10% of £129.50 = £12.95, 1% = £1.295 so 4% = £5.18. £12.95 + £5.18 = £18.13.)

   b) £147.63 (£129.50 + £18.13)

4. $\frac{1}{2}$ (There are 22 counters altogether. Of these, a total of 11 are either green or blue. $\frac{11}{22} = \frac{1}{2}$.)

5. **a)** $325\frac{2}{3}$ (the remainder becomes the numerator and the divisor becomes the denominator)

   b) $304\frac{1}{12}$ (the remainder becomes the numerator and the divisor becomes the denominator)

   c) 216 043

   d) 421 020

6. 900° (The 3 circles total 1080°. The triangle's angles = 180°, so 1080° − 180° = 900°.)

7. **a)** 79, 109 (add an extra 5 each time)

   b) $\frac{1}{4}, \frac{1}{8}$ (÷ 2)

8. **a)** 36 km/hr (15 km in 25 min = 3 km in 5 min = 36 km in 60 min)

   b) 25 km

   c) she stopped

   d) 48 km/hr (16 km in 20 min = 48 km in 60 min)

Section 3 Test 1 (page 28)

1. (1 mark for each correct answer. Max. 6 marks.)

UK pound (£)	South Africa rand (R)	Euro (€)	Japan yen (¥)
1	20	1.1	134
25	500	27.5	3350
51	1020	56.1	6834

2. 787 (BODMAS applies so $2 \times 7 = 14$, $14^2 = 196$, $196 \times 4 = 784$, $784 + 3 = 787$. BODMAS is explained on page A2, Section 1, Test 3, q1a).)

3. 646 ($925 - 367 = 558$, $558 \div 2 = 279$, $367 + 279 = 646$)

4. £180 290 (£134 565 + £45 725)

5. **a)** 9116 miles (4625 + 1398 + 3093)

b) 54 696 miles ($9116 \times 3 = 27 348$, $27 348 \times 2 = 54 696$)

6. 47 788 ($427 \times 2 = 854$, $46 934 + 854 = 47 788$)

7. 102 238 (3298×31)

8. **a)** 13 ($338 \div 26$)

b) 23 ($1081 \div 47$)

c) 16 ($624 \div 39$)

d) 21 ($1554 \div 74$)

9. 42 (work backwards: $129 - 17 = 112$, $112 \times 3 = 336$, $336 \div 8 = 42$)

10. 14 054.4 miles (The dog runs 19.2 miles on each walk, so 38.4 miles a day. 38.4 miles $\times$ 366 = 14 054.4 miles.)

11. 183m (He has made a total of £411.75. £411.75 $\div$ £2.25 = 183.)

Section 3 Test 2 (page 29)

1. **a)** $1\frac{7}{20}$ ($\frac{3}{5} = \frac{12}{20}$, $\frac{3}{4} = \frac{15}{20}$, so $\frac{12}{20} + \frac{15}{20} = \frac{27}{20} = 1\frac{7}{20}$)

b) $\frac{7}{8}$ ($\frac{1}{2} = \frac{4}{8}$, so $\frac{3}{8} + \frac{4}{8} = \frac{7}{8}$)

c) $\frac{7}{45}$ ($\frac{5}{9} = \frac{25}{45}$, $\frac{2}{5} = \frac{18}{45}$, so $\frac{25}{45} - \frac{18}{45} = \frac{7}{45}$)

d) $\frac{11}{21}$ ($\frac{2}{3} = \frac{14}{21}$, $\frac{1}{7} = \frac{3}{21}$, so $\frac{14}{21} - \frac{3}{21} = \frac{11}{21}$)

e) $\frac{3}{8}$ (multiply the numerators, then multiply the denominators, so $\frac{3}{4} \times \frac{1}{2} = \frac{3}{8}$)

f) $\frac{5}{48}$ (if each $\frac{1}{8}$ was split into 6, there would be 48 so $\frac{5}{8} \div 6 = \frac{5}{48}$)

2. 4.504 4.5 4.45 4.405 4.045 (To order easily, all decimals need the same number of digits after the decimal point. 4.45 and 4.5 only have 2 and 1 digit after the decimal while all the others have 3 digits so you need to put zeros on the end, e.g. 4.450 and 4.500. This does not change the value of the number. Now imagine the decimals are 4-digit whole numbers, e.g. 4405, 4504, 4450, 4045, 4500. Now put them in order.)

3. **a)** $\frac{1}{4}$

b) $\frac{5}{14}$

4. 754 (If 48% were boys then 52% were girls. 50% of 1450 = 725, 1% = 14.5 so 2% = 29. 725 + 29 = 754.)

5. (1 mark for each correct answer. Max. 5 marks. All the denominators must be converted to 100 using equivalence, e.g. Simon's score is $\frac{15}{24} = \frac{5}{8} = \frac{625}{1000} = \frac{62.5}{100} = 62.5\%$.)

Name	Score	Percentage
Simon	$\frac{15}{24}$	62.5%
Lucy	$\frac{56}{70}$	80%
Kaily	$\frac{36}{45}$	80%
Rafi	$\frac{12}{16}$	75%
Oli	$\frac{63}{90}$	70%

6. **a)** 112 (The ratio of 2:4:1 totals 7, so $392 \div 7 = 56$. $2 \times 56 = 112$.)

b) 224 (4×56)

c) 56 (1×56)

7. 0.000000001 sec

8. 2.79mm (0.04cm = 0.4mm, 0.1cm = 1mm, so 0.4mm + 1mm + 0.6mm + 0.09mm + 0.7mm = 2.79mm)

Answers

1. **a)** 3 (BODMAS applies so, working backwards, subtract 12, 57 − 12 = 45. Then 45 × 5 = 225. 15^2 = 225 so $5a$ must be 15 so a = 3. BODMAS is explained on page A2, Section 1, Test 3, q1a).)

   b) 12 (The equation needs to be simplified. First, + 36 to both sides so $(b + b^2)$ = 156. The squared number will need to be close to 156, e.g. 121 or 144. Hence b must be 12 as 12 + 144 = 156.)

   c) 7 (The equation needs to be simplified. There is $6c$ and $- 5c$ on the same side of the equation so that can be simplified to $1c$ or simply c. The equation is now $c + (c + 9)$ = 23. If you − 9 from both sides, you get $c + (c)$ = 14. The brackets are no longer needed so it becomes $c + c$ = 14 so c = 7.)

2. **a)** $3n + 3$

   b) $5n + 9$

   c) $4n + 4$

   d) $n^2 + 1$

3. **a)** (1 mark for each correct answer. Max. 3 marks.)

Shape	1	2	3	4	5	8	12
No. of dots	1	3	5	7	9	15	23

   b) $2n - 1$

   c) 199 (2 × 100 = 200, 200 − 1)

4. **a)** $6x + 4y$

   b) £46 (£6 × 5 = 30, £4 × 4 = 16, so £30 + £16 = £46)

5. **a)** $14x$ ($5x + 5x + 2x + 2x$)

   b) $10x^2$ ($5x × 2x$)

6. **a)** 53

   b) 64

   c) 75

   d) 0

1. £8.69 (£60.83 ÷ 7)

2. **a)** $113.04cm^2$ ($3.14 × 6^2$)

   b) $254.34cm^2$ ($3.14 × 9^2$)

3. 15.19cm (1st bounce = 36cm, 2nd bounce = 27cm, 3rd bounce = 20.25cm, 4th bounce = 15.1875cm)

4. **a)** 468km/hr (450km for 2 hr = 900km, 480km for 3 hr = 1440km, so in total 900km + 1440km = 2340km. 2340km ÷ 5 hr = 468km/hr.)

   b) 2340km

5. **a)** $125cm^3$ (5cm × 5cm × 5cm)

   b) $3375cm^3$ (15cm × 15cm × 15cm, not $125cm^3$ × 3)

6. 75 litres (If 264km = 40 litres, then 66km = 10 litres, 462km = 70 litres and 33km = 5 litres. 462km + 33km = 495km, so 70 litres + 5 litres = 75 litres.)

7. 2 hr 27 min (If uphill, 8 miles = 60 min, then 2 miles = 15 min, so 14 miles = 105 min. If downhill, 20 miles = 60 min, then 2 miles = 6 min, so 14 miles = 42 min. In total, 105 min + 42 min = 147 min = 2 hr and 27 min.)

8. **a)** Edinburgh (−7°C)

   b) 4°C (1°C − −3°C)

   c) Edinburgh (11°C)

   d) $\frac{2}{3}$°C (8°C in 12 hr)

9. (1 mark for each correct answer. Max. 6 marks.)

12-hour clock	24-hour clock
5:37 a.m.	05:37
4:27 p.m.	16:27
11:03 p.m.	23:03
11:19 p.m.	23:19
9:51 a.m.	09:51
12:31 a.m	00:31

Section 3 Test 5 (page 32)

1. a) (1 mark for each correct point plotted. Max. 4 marks.)

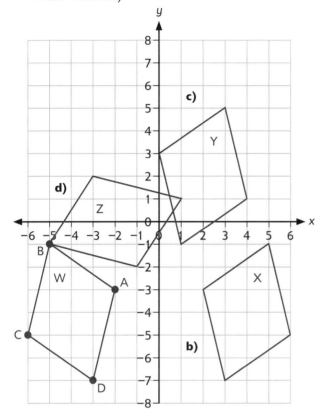

b) (1 mark for a correct reflection. See grid above.)

c) (1 mark for a correct translation. See grid above.)

d) (1 mark for a correct rotation. See grid above.)

2. a) 108° (The pentagon can be split into 5 isosceles triangles. Each point in the centre would be 72° as 360° ÷ 5 = 72°. The other 2 angles within each triangle must be 54° as 180° − 72° = 108° and 108° ÷ 2 = 54°. Angle A consists of 2 corners of the triangles so must be 108°.)

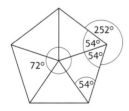

b) 1260° (If A is 108° then the external reflex angle must be 360° − 108° = 252°. There are 5 of them so 252° × 5 = 1260°.)

3. a) 111° (These cannot be worked out in order. Additional letters have been added to the diagram below to aid with explanation. The angles inside the quadrilateral that includes angle A = 360°. 44° [B] + 81° [Y: adds up to 180° with the angle of 99° adjacent on the straight line] + 124° [Z: alternate interior angles are equal] = 249°. 360° − 249° = 111°.)

b) 44° (X must be 44° as 136° + 44° = 180° and so B must also be 44° because when a line bisects a pair of parallel lines, the alternate interior angles are the same)

c) 56° (C must be 56° as 124° + 56° = 180°)

d) 99° (D must be 99° because when a line bisects a pair of parallel lines, the alternate interior angles are equal, so it is the same as the angle marked 99°)

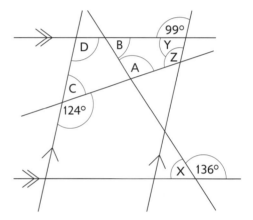

4. (1 mark for both the correct answer and line(s) of symmetry for each shape. Max. 6 marks.)

a) 0

b) 1

c) 6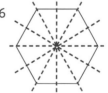

d) 4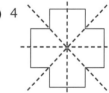

e) 0

f) 1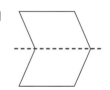

5. 24

Section 3 Test 6 (page 33)

1. a) 58 miles

    b) 213 miles

    c) 105 miles

    d) 102 miles

    e) 48 miles

    f) 56 miles

    g) Stranraer and Wick

2. a) 84kg (total weight of cricketers = 80kg × 3 = 240kg, 240kg + 516kg = 756kg, so 756kg ÷ 9 = 84kg)

    b) 756kg

3. 27 (20 + 22 + 24 + 26 + 28 + 30 + 32 + 34 = 216, 216 ÷ 8 = 27)

4. a) 8 (The section measures 30° = $\frac{1}{12}$ of the pie. 96 ÷ 12 = 8.)

    b) 20 (The section measures 75° = $\frac{5}{24}$ of the pie. 96 ÷ 24 = 4, 5 × 4 = 20.)

    c) 28 (The section measures 105° = $\frac{7}{24}$ of the pie. 96 ÷ 24 = 4, 7 × 4 = 28.)

    d) 24 (The section measures 90° = $\frac{1}{4}$ of the pie. 96 ÷ 4 = 24.)

    e) 16 (The section measures 60° = $\frac{1}{6}$ of the pie. 96 ÷ 6 = 16.)

5. a) December

    b) May

    c) November (£5400 − £3600 = £1800)

    d) £600 (£12 200 − £11 600)

    e) £31 200 (£2800 + £4600 + £4800 + £5200 + £6600 + £7200)

Section 3 Test 7 (page 34)

1. 6, 8, 10, 14, 15, 21, 22 (6 = 2 and 3, 8 = 2 and 4, 10 = 2 and 5, 14 = 2 and 7, 15 = 3 and 5, 21 = 3 and 7, 22 = 2 and 11)

2. a) 7.45m² (Split the compound shape into 2 rectangles. 6.46m² + 0.99m² = 7.45m².)

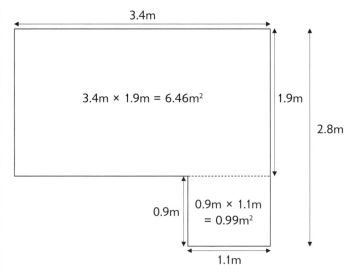

    b) 21 (60cm × 60cm = 0.6m × 0.6m = 0.36m², so 7.45m² ÷ 0.36m² = 20 r.25 so he would need 21 slabs)

    c) £23.52 (£1.12 × 21)

3. 0.8 ($\frac{12}{15} = \frac{4}{5} = \frac{8}{10}$ = 0.8)

4. $\frac{191}{500}$ (0.382 = $\frac{382}{1000} = \frac{191}{500}$)

5. 32.5% ($\frac{26}{80} = \frac{13}{40} = \frac{6.5}{20} = \frac{32.5}{100}$ = 32.5%)

6. a) 504 (b) has to be worked out first. 267 + 377 = 644, 1148 − 644 = 504.)

    b) 377 (312 + 459 = 771, 1148 − 771 = 377)

7. a) 1:500 (2m:1000m = 1m:500m)

    b) 1:9 (10 sec:90 sec = 1 sec:9 sec)

    c) 9:40 (450ml:2000ml = 9ml:40ml)

8. 525kg ($\frac{1}{8}$kg = 125g, 125g × 100 horses = 12 500g = 12.5kg, 12.5kg × 42 days = 525kg)

9. a) 300km (1 hr = 120km, 2 hr = 240km, $\frac{1}{2}$ hr = 60km, so 240km + 60km = 300km)

    b) 390km (1 hr = 120km, 3 hr = 360km, $\frac{1}{4}$ hr = 30km, so 360km + 30km = 390km)

    c) 144km (1 hr = 120km, $\frac{1}{5}$ hr = 24km, so 120km + 24km = 144km)

10. 28.8kg (3.2kg × 9)

11. a) 1.5

    b) 2.45

    c) 2.375

Section 3 Test 8 (page 35)

1. **a)** 5, 0, 3 (4526 × 9 = 40 734)

   b) 4, 4 (5894 ÷ 7 = 842)

2. **a)** 26 hours (156 ÷ 6 = 26)

   b) 180m/min (60m/20 sec × 3 = 180m/min)

   c) 67.5km (45km/hr = 22.5km/$\frac{1}{2}$ hr, so 45km + 22.5km = 67.5km)

3. 2210 (136 loaves in 12 min = 680 loaves in 1 hr = 2040 loaves in 3 hr. Also 170 loaves in 15 min, so 2040 + 170 = 2210.)

4. **a)** 60 (The ratio 5:3:6 totals 14. 168 ÷ 14 = 12, so 5 × 12 = 60.)

   b) 36 (3 × 12 = 36)

   c) 72 (6 × 12 = 72)

5. **a)** 7 (if x^2 + 12 = 61, then x^2 = 49, $\sqrt{49}$ = 7)

   b) 26 (26 + 40 = 66)

   c) 22 (3b + c is the same as 3b + 2b as c is the same as 2b. So 5b = 55, so b = 11, so c = 22.)

6. **a)** 44.8m² (Split the compound shape into 2 rectangles. 35m² + 9.8m² = 44.8m².)

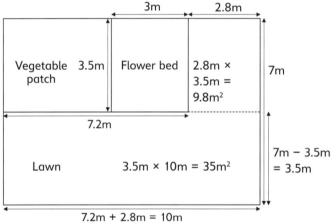

   b) 34m (10m + 7m + 2.8m + 3.5m + 7.2m + 3.5m)

   c) $\frac{3}{20}$ (The entire area is 10m × 7m = 70m², the flower bed is 3m × 3.5m = 10.5m². $\frac{10.5}{70}$ = $\frac{21}{140}$ = $\frac{3}{20}$.)

   d) 4 (The veg patch is 4.2m × 3.5m = 14.7m². Each bag covers 4m² so she would need 4 bags to cover the entire patch.)

7. £605 500 (if $\frac{2}{7}$ = £173 000, then $\frac{1}{7}$ = £86 500, so $\frac{7}{7}$ = £605 500)

8. **a)** 9 (8 + 12 + 5 + 9 + 13 + 7 = 54 ÷ 6 = 9)

   b) 8.5 (The median is the middle value when the numbers are put in order: 5, 7, 8, 9, 12, 13. The middle number would be halfway between 8 and 9 so 8.5.)

   c) 16 (If the mean after 7 matches was 10, then the total number of goals after 7 matches was 70. She had scored 54 after 6 matches so must have scored 16 in the 7th match.)

Section 3 Test 9 (page 36)

1. **a)** 5 (bars under the horizontal line)

   b) November (−£50)

   c) £45 (£90 − £45)

   d) February and March (£65 to −£45 = £110)

   e) July and August (−£40 to £80 = £120)

2. **a)** 34 (The ratio is 2:3:4 which totals 9, so 153 ÷ 9 = 17. 17 × 2 = 34.)

   b) 51 (17 × 3 = 51)

   c) 68 (17 × 4 = 68)

3. 70p (if 3$\frac{1}{4}$l = £4.55, then divide by 13 = $\frac{1}{4}$l = 35p, so $\frac{1}{2}$l = 70p)

4. 77 (234 ÷ 3 = 78, so 78 is the middle number so 77 must be the smallest number)

5. 4$\frac{1}{8}$ (5$\frac{1}{2}$ − 2$\frac{3}{4}$ = 2$\frac{3}{4}$. 2$\frac{3}{4}$ ÷ 2 = 1$\frac{3}{8}$, 2$\frac{3}{4}$ + 1$\frac{3}{8}$ = 4$\frac{1}{8}$)

6. **a)** £1.35 (10% of £1.20 = 12p, 5% = 6p, 2.5% = 3p so 12.5% = 12p + 3p = 15p. £1.20 + 15p = £1.35.)

   b) 42p (10% of 30p = 3p, so 40% = 12p. 30p + 12p = 42p.)

   c) 62p (10% of 50p = 5p, 1% = 0.5p, so 20% = 10p and 4% = 2p so 10p + 2p = 12p. 50p + 12p = 62p.)

   d) £1.16 (10% of 80p = 8p, so 40% = 32p, 5% = 4p, so 32p + 4p = 36p. 80p + 36p = £1.16.)

   e) £3.40 (10% of £2.50 = 25p, so 30% = 75p. 1% = 2.5p so 6% = 15p. 75p + 15p = 90p so £2.50 + 90p = £3.40.)

7. **a)** 15:50 (her watch has moved on 8 min, so should have moved forward 16 min)

   b) 18:18 (her watch has moved on 1 hr 22 min, so should have moved forward 2 hr 44 min)

   c) 15:41 (the actual time has moved on 14 min, so her watch will only have moved on 7 min)

   d) 16:30 (the actual time has moved on 1 hr 52 min, so her watch will only have moved on 56 min)

Section 3 Test 10 (page 37)

1. **a)** (1 mark for each correct point plotted.
Max. 3 marks.)

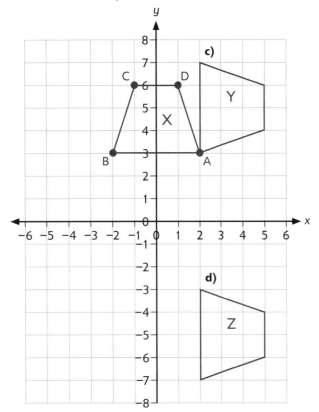

b) (1 mark for a correct point plotted and shape
drawn. See grid above.)

c) (1 mark for a correct rotation. See grid above.)

d) (1 mark for a correct reflection. See grid above.)

e) (2, −7) (2, −3) (5, −4) (5, −6) in any order
(1 mark for each correct coordinate.
Max. 4 marks.)

2. 12.5% $\frac{3}{8}$ $\frac{2}{5}$ 0.42 0.65 (convert them all into
the same number type, e.g. percentages, so $\frac{2}{5}$
= 40%, 0.65 = 65%, $\frac{3}{8}$ = 37.5%, 0.42 = 42%)

3. 280 800 sec (1 min = 60 sec, 1 hr = 3600 sec,
1 day = 86 400 sec, so 3 days = 259 200 sec. $\frac{1}{4}$ day
= 6 hr = 21 600 sec, so 259 200 sec + 21 600 sec =
280 800 sec.)

4. 80p (she spent $\frac{5}{8}$ + $\frac{1}{5}$ = $\frac{25}{40}$ + $\frac{8}{40}$ = $\frac{33}{40}$ so she has
$\frac{7}{40}$ left = 14p, so $\frac{1}{40}$ = 2p, therefore she must have
started with 80p)

5. 14.44cm² (15.2cm ÷ 4 = 3.8cm, 3.8cm × 3.8cm
= 14.44cm²)

6. 216 (the numbers are cubed numbers getting
progressively bigger from the top right-hand corner
to the bottom left-hand corner)

7. **a)** 2n + 4

b) 56 (26 × 2 = 52, 52 + 4 = 56)

c) 60 (work backwards: 124 − 4 = 120, 120 ÷ 2
= 60)

8. **a)** 432 (BODMAS applies so 5 + 7 = 12, 12² =
144, 6 ÷ 2 = 3, so 144 × 3 = 432. BODMAS is
explained on page A2, Section 1, Test 3, q1a).)

b) 33 (BODMAS applies so 3³ = 27, 9 × 8 = 72, 72
÷ 12 = 6, so 27 + 6 = 33. BODMAS is explained
on page A2, Section 1, Test 3, q1a).)

Section 3 Test 11 (page 38)

1. 190 (1050cm ÷ 5.5)

2. 225, 675 (the digits of numbers divisible by 3 add
up to 3, 6 and 9, numbers divisible by 5 end in 5
or 0, and all digits of numbers that are divisible by
9 add up to 9 or a multiple of 9)

3. 60cm (5cm × 5cm × 5cm = 125cm², so 12 edges at
5cm each = 60cm)

4. 1001 (1000 ÷ 11 = 90 r.10. Therefore 11 × 10 =
990 and 11 × 91 = 1001, which is closer to 1000.)

5. **a)** XXXIV, XLII (add 1 more each time)

b) 10.8, 12.1 (+ 1.3)

6. **a)** $2\frac{7}{12}$ ($1\frac{3}{4}$ = $\frac{7}{4}$ = $\frac{21}{12}$, $\frac{5}{6}$ = $\frac{10}{12}$, so $\frac{21}{12}$ + $\frac{10}{12}$ = $\frac{31}{12}$ =
$2\frac{7}{12}$)

b) $\frac{9}{10}$ ($2\frac{1}{2}$ = $\frac{5}{2}$ = $\frac{25}{10}$, $1\frac{3}{5}$ = $\frac{8}{5}$ = $\frac{16}{10}$, so $\frac{25}{10}$ − $\frac{16}{10}$ = $\frac{9}{10}$)

c) $\frac{5}{18}$ (multiply the numerators, then multiply the
denominators)

d) $\frac{3}{40}$ ($\frac{1}{4}$ split into 10 would give $\frac{1}{40}$ so $\frac{3}{10}$ ÷ 4 = $\frac{3}{40}$)

7. 450cm² (The pentagon can be divided into 5 equal
triangles. The area of each is 15cm × 12cm = 180cm²,
180cm² ÷ 2 = 90cm². 90cm² × 5 = 450cm².)

8. £600 (£175 × 36 = £6300, £6300 + £1050 =
£7350, £7350 − £6750 = £600)

9. £47.60 (10% of £56 = £5.60, 5% = £2.80, so 15%
= £8.40. £56 − £8.40 = £47.60.)

10. 1.015km (Between 30 trees there will be 29 spaces.
29 × 35m = 1015m = 1.015km.)

11. a) 3 (first, − 3 from both sides so $2x + 3 = 3x$, then − $2x$ from both sides so $x = 3$)

b) 5 (first, + 4 to both sides so $4x = 3x + 5$, then − $3x$ from both sides so $x = 5$)

c) 2 (first, + 3 to both sides so $6x + 4 = 8x$, then − $6x$ from both sides so $4 = 2x$, therefore $x = 2$)

12. a) 89.17 (when the thousandths are 4 or less, the number is rounded down to the existing hundredth)

b) 52.63 (when the thousandths are 5 or more, the number is rounded up to the next hundredth)

13. 112cm² (A kite consists of 2 triangles. The top triangle measures 12cm × 8cm so the area is $12 × 8 ÷ 2 = 48$cm². The bottom triangle measures 16cm × 8cm so the area is $16 × 8 ÷ 2 = 64$cm². 64 cm² + 48 cm² = 112cm².)

Section 3 Test 12 (page 39)

1. 0.625 ($\frac{1}{8} = 0.125$)

2. $2 × 2 × 3 × 5 × 5$

3. 15m/sec (54km/hr = 54km/60 min = 9km/10 min = 0.9km/1 min = 900m/60 sec = 15m/sec)

4. a) 2

b) $7y^3$

5. a) 150

b) 8

c) 4

6. a) 135° (These cannot be worked out in order. Additional letters have been added to the diagram below to aid with explanation. A is double angle B so 135°.)

b) 67.5° (If C = 45° then X + Y = 135° [180° − 45°] so both are 67.5°. So B must also be 67.5°.)

c) 45° (C must be 45° as 8 triangles can be created so each centre angle would be 45° as 360° ÷ 8 = 45°)

d) 67.5° (D will be 1.5 × C so 67.5°)

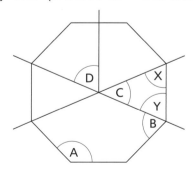

7. 26 ($\frac{7}{8}$l = 875ml so 22.75l ÷ 875ml = 26)

8. £4.65 (Halve the second order so that the drinks are the same. 3 chicken wraps and 2 drinks = £8.35, 2 chicken wraps and 2 drinks = £6.10. The difference is 1 chicken wrap and £2.25 so a chicken wrap must cost £2.25. So, 2 chicken wraps = £4.50, so 2 drinks = £1.60, therefore 1 drink = 80p. 1 chicken wrap and 3 drinks = £2.25 + £2.40 = £4.65.)

9. a) 24°C (25°C − 1°C)

b) December (14°C difference)

c) 39°C (28°C − −11°C)

d) −2°C (in the month of May)

10. a) −35

b) 3 (when 2 minuses are together, it makes a plus)

Answers

This book of answers is a pull-out section from **Maths Rapid Tests 6**.

Published by **Schofield & Sims Ltd**,
7 Mariner Court, Wakefield, West Yorkshire WF4 3FL, UK
Telephone 01484 607080
www.schofieldandsims.co.uk

This edition copyright © Schofield & Sims Ltd, 2018
First published in 2018
Second impression 2019

Author: **Rebecca Brant**. Rebecca Brant has asserted her moral rights under the
Copyright, Designs and Patents Act, 1988, to be identified as the author of this work.

British Library Cataloguing in Publication Data. A catalogue record for this book
is available from the British Library.

Design by **Ledgard Jepson Ltd**
Printed in the UK by **Page Bros (Norwich) Ltd**

ISBN 978 07217 1426 4

Target time: **8 minutes**

1. A group of children were asked which sports they played. Write the information in the Venn diagram.

   a) 16 played both rounders and football.

   b) 20 played both rounders and netball.

   c) 2 played all three sports.

   d) Only 1 person just played netball.

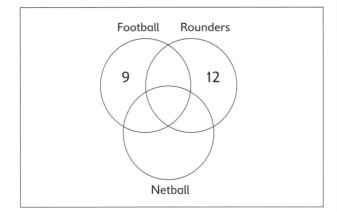

   e) If a total of 76 children were asked, how many children played netball and football? _____

2. Match the pie charts to the bar charts.

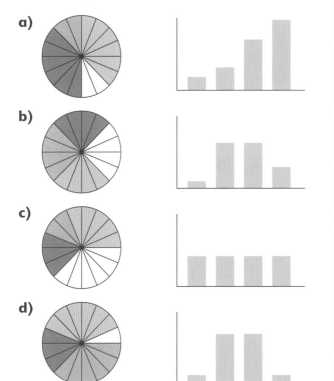

3. Leo rode his scooter from his house and back.

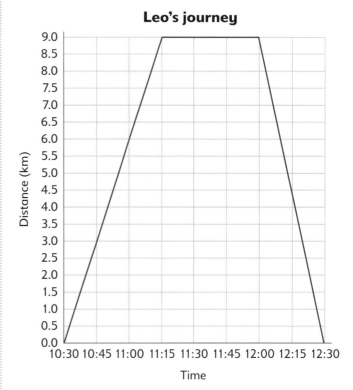

   a) How far is Zac's house from Leo's? _____

   b) How long did it take Leo to get to Zac's house? _____

   c) How fast did he travel to get there? _____

   d) How long did he stay there? _____

   e) How long did it take him to get home? _____

   f) How fast was he travelling on the way home? _____

4. The average number of runs Jack scored in six games of cricket was 36. He scored 18 in his first game, twice that in his second game and two and a half times that in his third game. In his final three games, he scored the same number of runs each game. What were his scores?

Game 1	Game 2	Game 3	Game 4	Game 5	Game 6
18					

Score:		Time taken:		Target met?	

Target time: **8 minutes**

1. The local gym had 560 members. Three hundred and sixty-four of the members were women.

   a) What percentage of the members were men? _____

   b) If each member paid a monthly subscription of £35, how much money did the gym make each month? _____

2. The following pattern represents triangular numbers.

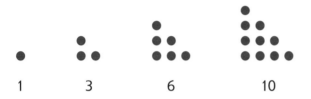

   1   3   6   10

   The formula for this pattern is $\frac{n(n+1)}{2}$.

   a) What would the 10th number be? _____

   b) What would the 100th number be? _____

3. Adam drives from London to Edinburgh. He is averaging 63 miles per hour and has been travelling for 2 hours and 20 minutes when he gets a puncture. He still has 267 miles to go. How far is it from London to Edinburgh? _____

4. Underline the square numbers and circle the cube numbers.

   1   4   8   16   25   37   64   91

5. How many hours are there in a fortnight? _____

6. How many hours are there in 3 weeks and 4 days? _____

7. How many days are there in 4 consecutive years? _____

8. How many seconds are there in 1 day? _____

9. The compound shape below has an area of 154cm². What is the missing measurement?

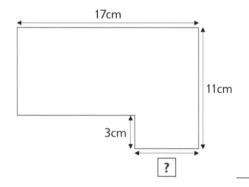

   _____

10. What is the lowest common multiple of 9 and 12? _____

11. What is the highest common factor of 24 and 132? _____

12. Which multiple of 3 is closest to 800? _____

13. What number is halfway between 134 and 456? _____

14. Solve these calculations.

   a) $\frac{5}{9} + \frac{2}{3} =$ _____

   b) $\frac{7}{12} \div 3 =$ _____

   c) $\frac{2}{7} \times \frac{3}{4} =$ _____

   d) $\frac{1}{2} - \frac{1}{6} =$ _____

Score: _____   Time taken: _____   Target met? _____

Target time: **8 minutes**

1. Anita asked 168 children in her school to vote for their favourite animal. The pie chart shows the results.

Favourite animals

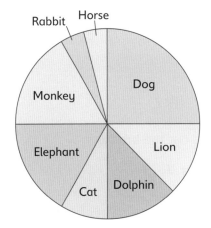

a) If the same number of children voted for a horse and a rabbit, how many voted for a rabbit? _____

b) How many children voted for a dog? _____

c) What percentage voted for a dolphin? _____

d) What fraction voted for a cat? _____

e) How many children like elephants best? _____

2. Frank is laying a wooden floor in a friend's kitchen. The kitchen measures 3m long by 2.5m wide. The wooden flooring comes in planks that are 1.2m long and 0.25m wide.

a) What is the total length of wooden planks Frank will need? _____

b) How many planks will Frank need? _____

3. Complete these sequences.

a) 1, 8, 27, 64, 125, _____, _____

b) 5, 7, 11, 17, 25, _____, _____

4. Round these numbers to two decimal places.

a) 173.015 _____

b) 35.945 _____

c) 69.378 _____

d) 437.823 _____

5. The following plan shows Joe's garden.

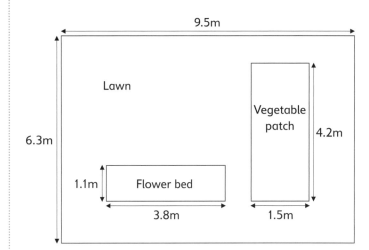

a) What is the area of the vegetable patch? _____

b) What is the area of the lawn? _____

c) Joe wants to put edging around the flower bed and vegetable patch. What length of edging does he need to buy? _____

d) Edging is sold in whole metres at a cost of £3.15 per metre. How much will Joe have to pay? _____

6. Write the correct operation signs to make these calculations correct.

a) 7 _____ 3 _____ 4 _____ 9 = 16

b) 16 _____ 4 _____ 8 _____ 6 = 38

7. What is 7^3? _____

Score:	Time taken:	Target met?

Target time: **8 minutes**

1. The total ages of a mother, her daughter and twin sons is 104. If the daughter is half the age of her mother but twice the age of her twin brothers, how old is each person?

a) Mother _____

b) Daughter _____

c) Sons _____

2. Freda wanted to buy a new car. She saw one advertised for £7890. She offered the owner 15% less. How much did she offer? _____

3. Gloria is travelling 1456km on her trip. She has already travelled 598km. How much further does she have to go? _____

4. Ed did a paper round where he was paid £4.48 an hour plus an extra 8p for every newspaper he delivered. It took him $1\frac{3}{4}$ hours a day to deliver 123 newspapers and he worked every day except Sunday. How much did he earn each week? _____

5. Write the time difference between each pair of clocks.

a)

_____

b)
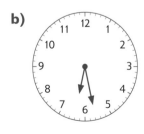 

_____

6. What is the area of the parallelogram?

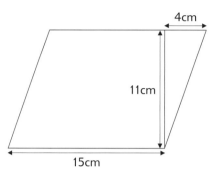

_____

7. Multiply out the brackets.

a) $3(2a + 4b) =$ _____

b) $4(3a + 2b) =$ _____

8. Write the missing number to solve these calculations.

a) $\dfrac{4}{5} + \dfrac{\boxed{?}}{15} = \dfrac{14}{15}$ _____

b) $\dfrac{3}{8} + \dfrac{\boxed{?}}{16} = \dfrac{9}{16}$ _____

9. Solve these calculations.

a) $1373 \times 5.7 =$ _____

b) $3384 \div 36 =$ _____

10. A palindromic number is one that can be read the same backwards and forwards, for example, 121.

a) What is the next palindromic number after 1221? _____

b) What is the next palindromic number after 13431? _____

c) Calculate the sum of all the palindromic numbers between 150 and 200. _____

11. What is the value of each underlined digit?

a) 73930637 _____

b) 142730867 _____

Score: _____ Time taken: _____ Target met? _____

Target time: **8 minutes**

1. Use the equation to complete the table.

$y = 4x - 6$

x	7	12	
y			6

2. Each row and column adds up to 28.

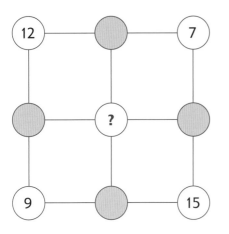

What is the missing number? _____

3. A sofa factory made 15 sofas a day at a cost of £215 a sofa. The sofas were then sold at a 30% profit.

a) What did each sofa sell for? _____

b) How much profit did the factory make each day? _____

4. Find these amounts.

a) What is 30% of £8.90? _____

b) What is 45% of £5.60? _____

c) What is 62% of £6.50? _____

5. Write these numbers as products of their prime factors.

a) 21 _____

b) 45 _____

c) 12 _____

6. What is the volume of this triangular prism?

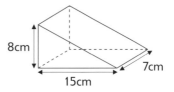

_____

7. The bus timetable shows buses from Cambridge Street to Alton Avenue.

	A	B	C	D
Cambridge Street	08:35	08:56	09:24	09:48
Frogmore Road	08:46	–	09:35	09:59
Leedown Lane	–	09:15	–	10:09
High Street	09:02	09:24	–	–
French Street	09:13	09:35	10:01	10:26
Hendon Road	–	09:43	10:09	–
Alton Avenue	09:25	–	10:13	10:38

a) How long does the 08:56 bus from Cambridge Street take to get to French Street? _____

b) Kalyn needs to be in Leedown Lane for an appointment at 09:30. Which bus does she need to get from Cambridge Street? _____

c) Which is the fastest bus from Frogmore Road to Alton Avenue? _____

d) The 09:24 from the High Street is running 7 minutes late. At what time will it arrive in Hendon Road? _____

8. The mass of 2 bags of flour and 3 apples is 1110g. The mass of 3 bags of flour and 6 apples is 1770g.

a) What is the mass of 1 bag of flour? _____

b) What is the mass of 1 apple? _____

9. What is $\frac{1}{2}$ of $\frac{1}{3}$ of 48? _____

Score:		Time taken:		Target met?	

Target time: **8 minutes**

1. Rehma earns £22 670 a year. She receives a 1.5% pay rise.

a) How much does she earn now? _____

b) If she gets taxed 20% of her total earnings, how much does she actually take home in a year? _____

c) How much is this per month to the nearest whole pound? _____

2. Write these decimals in descending order.

12.1   1.21   2.12   12.01   12.2

_____

3. Solve these calculations.

a) 12.3 × _____ = 1230

b) 153 ÷ _____ = 0.153

4. The following pattern represents square numbers.

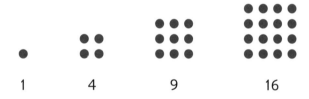

1   4   9   16

What would the formula be for finding the nth term?

_____

5. What is the name of the shape that this net creates?

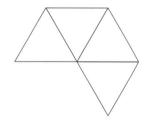

_____

6. House prices have risen by 2%. What price would a house previously costing £540 000 now cost? _____

7. Calculate the missing angles.

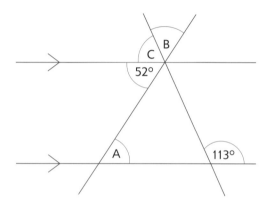

a) A = _____   **b)** B = _____

c) C = _____

8. Look at the following sequence.

12, 5, −2, −9

a) What would the 7th term be? _____

b) What would the 50th term be? _____

9. Complete the table. Write each fraction in its simplest form.

Fraction	Decimal	Percentage
$\frac{9}{30}$		
	0.125	
		74%

Score: _____   Time taken: _____   Target met? _____

Target time: **8 minutes**

1. Write the numbers 1–10 inclusive in the correct section of the Carroll diagram.

	Odd	**Not odd**
Prime		
Not prime		

2. Simplify these formulae.

a) $5e \times 5e$ _____

b) $2a + 3a \times 5$ _____

3. If Aliya saves her birthday money, her mum will increase it by 14%. Aliya is given £36 by her grandmother, £27 by her aunt, £52.20 by her uncle and £14.30 by her sister.

a) How much money does her mother give her? _____

b) How much does she have in total now? _____

4. There are 6 red counters, 4 green counters, 5 yellow counters and 7 blue counters in a bag. What is the probability of picking out either a green or a blue counter? Write the answer as a fraction in its simplest form. _____

5. Solve these calculations and write any remainders as a fraction.

a) $6 \overline{)1\ 9\ 5\ 4}$ _____

b) $1\ 2 \overline{)3\ 6\ 4\ 9}$ _____

c)
$$\begin{array}{r} 5\ 8\ 3\ 9 \\ \times\qquad 3\ 7 \\ \hline \\ \hline \end{array}$$

d)
$$\begin{array}{r} 9\ 3\ 5\ 6 \\ \times\qquad 4\ 5 \\ \hline \\ \hline \end{array}$$

6. Calculate the sum of all three angles shown.

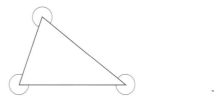

_____

7. Complete these sequences.

a) 4, 9, 19, 34, 54, _____, _____

b) 16, 8, 4, 2, 1, $\frac{1}{2}$, _____, _____

8. This line graph shows Tia's cycle journey.

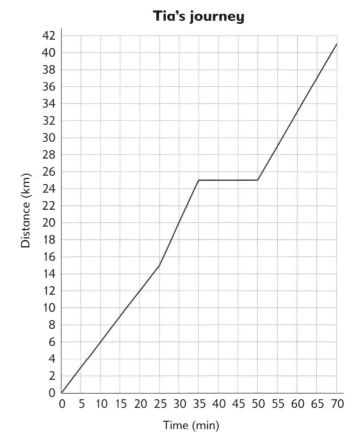

a) At what speed was she travelling for the first 25 minutes? _____

b) How far did she travel during the first 35 minutes? _____

c) What happened 35 minutes into her journey? _____

d) Between 50 and 70 minutes, how fast was Helen travelling? _____

Score:		Time taken:		Target met?	

1. Complete the table to convert the currency.

UK pound (£)	South Africa rand (R)	Euro (€)	Japan yen (¥)
1	20	1.1	134
25			
51			

2. Solve this calculation.

$3 + 4(2 \times 7)^2 =$ _____

3. What number is halfway between 367 and 925? _____

4. Gerry bought a house for £134 565 four years ago. He has just been told that its value has increased by £45 725. What is it worth now? _____

5. A pilot flies 4625 miles to his first destination, 1398 miles to his next and then 3093 miles to his final destination.

a) How far has he flown in total? _____

b) He makes this journey three times a week. How far does he travel in a fortnight? _____

6. The milometer in Yan's car shows that it has travelled 46 934 miles. Yan is going to drive to visit a friend in Edinburgh, which is 427 miles away. What will the reading on her milometer be when she returns from Edinburgh? _____

7. A tyre factory produced 3298 tyres a day. How many did they produce in March? _____

8. Solve these calculations.

a) $26 \times$ _____ $= 338$

b) _____ $\times 47 = 1081$

c) $624 \div$ _____ $= 39$

d) $1554 \div$ _____ $= 74$

9. Complete this function machine.

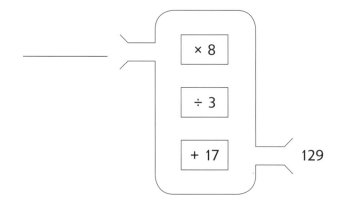

_____ × 8

÷ 3

+ 17   129

10. Runa walks with her dog for 4 miles, twice a day, every day. Runa's dog, Jake, likes to run around and for every mile Runa walks, Jake runs 4.8 miles. How far will Jake have run over the course of a leap year? _____

11. Serj painted his neighbours' fences to earn some extra pocket money. He charged £2.25 for every metre he painted. The table below shows how much money he has made.

Week 1	Week 2	Week 3
£108	£166.50	£137.25

Over the course of three weeks, how many metres of fence has he painted? _____

Score:		Time taken:		Target met?	

Target time: **8 minutes**

1. Solve these calculations and write each answer in its simplest form.

    a) $\frac{3}{5} + \frac{3}{4} =$ _____

    b) $\frac{3}{8} + \frac{1}{2} =$ _____

    c) $\frac{5}{9} - \frac{2}{5} =$ _____

    d) $\frac{2}{3} - \frac{1}{7} =$ _____

    e) $\frac{3}{4} \times \frac{1}{2} =$ _____

    f) $\frac{5}{8} \div 6 =$ _____

2. Write these decimals in descending order.

    4.405   4.504   4.45   4.045   4.5

    _____

3. What fraction of each of these shapes is shaded?

    a)

    _____

    b)

    _____

4. In a school of 1450 children, 48% of the children were boys. How many were girls?   _____

5. Calculate the percentages these children got in their exams.

Name	Score	Percentage
Simon	$\frac{15}{24}$	
Lucy	$\frac{56}{70}$	
Kaily	$\frac{36}{45}$	
Rafi	$\frac{12}{16}$	
Oli	$\frac{63}{90}$	

6. Reema, Laura and Thea collected 392 conkers between them in a ratio of 2:4:1. Calculate how many conkers each girl collected.

    a) Reema   _____

    b) Laura   _____

    c) Thea   _____

7. A computer processes information in nanoseconds. That is one billionth of a second. Write this number as a decimal.

    _____

8. The measurements below are the thicknesses of 5 pieces of paper.

0.04cm	0.6mm	0.1cm
	0.09mm	0.7mm

    What is the combined thickness of these 5 pieces of paper? Write the answer in millimetres.   _____

Score:	Time taken:	Target met?

Target time: **8 minutes**

1. Solve these equations.

   a) $(5a)^2 \div 5 + 12 = 57$ $a =$ _____

   b) $(b + b^2) - 36 = 120$ $b =$ _____

   c) $6c + (c + 9) - 5c = 23$ $c =$ _____

2. Write the formula to describe each sequence.

   a) 6, 9, 12, 15, 18

            nth term = _____

   b) 14, 19, 24, 29, 34

            nth term = _____

   c) 8, 12, 16, 20, 24

            nth term = _____

   d) 2, 5, 10, 17, 26

            nth term = _____

3. Look at this pattern.

   a) Complete the table.

Shape	1	2	3	4	5	8	12
No. of dots	1	3	5	7			

   b) What would the formula be for finding the nth number? _____

   c) How many dots would the 100th shape have? _____

4. Craig is going to order some flowers (£6) and some chocolates (£4).

   a) Write an algebraic formula to find the total cost if Craig buys x flowers and y chocolates.

   _____

   b) What will the total cost be if $x = 5$ and $y = 4$? _____

5. Look at the rectangle below.

   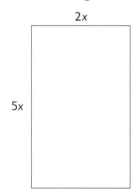

   2x

   5x

   a) What is the perimeter of the rectangle? _____

   b) What is the area of the rectangle? _____

6. If $a = 12$, $b = 16$, $c = 3$ and $d = 9$, solve these equations.

   a) $(a + 2b) + c^2 =$ _____

   b) $d^2 - 3a + (b + c) =$ _____

   c) $bc + c^3 =$ _____

   d) $4d + a - cb =$ _____

Score: _____   **Time taken:** _____   **Target met?** _____

Target time: **8 minutes**

1. Lisa has £60.83 to spend on presents for her 7 friends. She spends the same on each present. How much does each one cost? _____

2. The area of a circle can be calculated with the following formula.

   $3.14 \times r^2$ (where r = radius)

   What is the area of each of these circles?

   a)

   12cm
   _____

   b)
   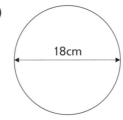
   18cm
   _____

3. A ball is dropped from a height of 48cm. Each time it bounces it reaches $\frac{3}{4}$ of its previous height. How high will it bounce after the 4th bounce? Write the answer correct to two decimal places. _____

4. An aircraft flies at an average speed of 450km per hour for 2 hours. For the next 3 hours, it speeds up to an average speed of 480km per hour.

   a) What is the average speed for the entire journey? _____

   b) How far does the plane travel? _____

5. Cube A has edges that are 5cm long. Cube B has edges 3 times as long.

   a) What is the volume of Cube A? _____

   b) What is the volume of Cube B? _____

6. If a car uses 40 litres of fuel when travelling 264km, how much fuel would it use over 495km? _____

7. Jimmy cycled uphill for 14 miles at a speed of 8 miles per hour. He then cycled back down the hill at a speed of 20 miles per hour. How long did it take him to travel up and down the hill? _____

8. The chart below shows the temperature in °C in four capital cities.

	01:00	13:00
London	−3	5
Edinburgh	−7	4
Cardiff	−1	6
Belfast	1	3

   a) Which city experienced the lowest temperature? _____

   b) How much warmer was it in Belfast at 1 a.m. compared to London at 1 a.m.? _____

   c) Which city had the greatest rise in temperature? _____

   d) What was the average hourly temperature increase in London? _____

9. Convert these times.

12-hour clock	24-hour clock
5:37 a.m.	
	16:27
	23:03
11:19 p.m.	
9:51 a.m.	
	00:31

Score: _____ Time taken: _____ Target met? _____

Target time: **8 minutes**

1. a) Plot, label and join the following points and label the shape W.

A (−2, −3) B (−5, −1) C (−6, −5) D (−3, −7)

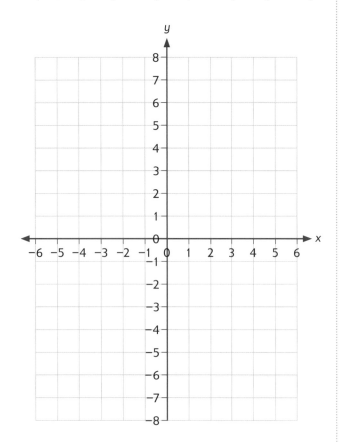

b) Reflect shape W in the y axis and label it shape X.

c) Translate shape X U6 L2 and label it shape Y.

d) Rotate shape W 90° anticlockwise about point B and label it shape Z.

2. The following shape is a regular pentagon.

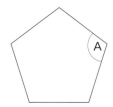

a) What size is angle A? _____

b) What would be the total of all the external reflex angles? _____

3. Calculate the missing angles.

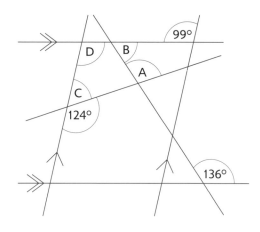

a) A = _____   **b)** B = _____

c) C = _____   **d)** D = _____

4. Draw any lines of symmetry on these shapes and write the number of lines underneath.

a)   **b)**

_____   _____

c)    **d)**

_____   _____

e)   **f)**

_____   _____

5. How many edges are there in an octagonal prism? _____

Score: _____   **Time taken:** _____   **Target met?** _____

Target time: **8 minutes**

1. The chart below shows the driving distances in miles between Scottish cities.

	Aberdeen	Dundee	Edinburgh	Fort William	Glasgow	Inverness	Oban	Perth	Stirling	Stranraer	Ullapool	Wick
Aberdeen	0											
Dundee	66	0										
Edinburgh	125	56	0									
Fort William	156	117	135	0								
Glasgow	147	76	48	102	0							
Inverness	105	129	157	65	173	0						
Oban	182	120	122	45	97	109	0					
Perth	87	26	42	102	62	114	94	0				
Stirling	120	58	38	97	29	144	86	33	0			
Stranraer	232	102	133	188	86	258	173	146	114	0		
Ullapool	157	182	209	121	223	56	166	167	197	308	0	
Wick	208	229	260	167	276	105	213	216	245	361	121	0

How far is it between these towns?

a) Dundee and Stirling _____

b) Oban and Wick _____

c) Inverness and Aberdeen _____

d) Fort William and Perth _____

e) Edinburgh and Glasgow _____

f) Ullapool and Inverness _____

g) Between which 2 towns is the greatest distance?

_____

2. The total weight of 6 footballers is 516kg and the mean weight of 3 cricketers is 80kg.

a) What is the mean weight of all 9 sportspersons? _____

b) What is the total weight of all 9 sportspersons? _____

3. Find the mean of all the even numbers between 19 and 35. _____

4. A shop has 96 jumpers in stock. Use a protractor to calculate how many of each size they have. Complete the table below.

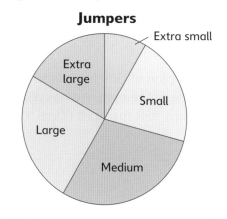

Jumpers

X Small	Small	Medium	Large	X Large
a)	b)	c)	d)	e)

5. This graph shows the monthly income of a farm.

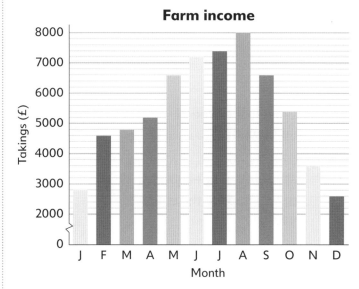

Farm income

a) In which month did the farm make the least money? _____

b) In which month was £1400 more made than the month before? _____

c) In which month was the biggest drop in income seen? _____

d) How much more was made in the first 3 months than the last 3 months? _____

e) How much money was made in the first half of the year? _____

Score:		Time taken:		Target met?	

Target time: **8 minutes**

1. List all the positive integers less than 25 that only have 2 different factors (not including 1 and itself).

_____

2. Below is a plan of Gethin's garden. He wants to pave the entire area. He has chosen paving slabs that measure 60cm × 60cm.

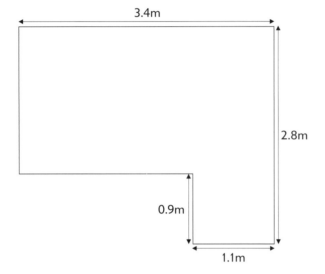

3.4m

2.8m

0.9m

1.1m

a) What is the area of his garden? _____

b) What is the fewest number of paving slabs he will need to buy to pave the entire garden? _____

c) The local garden centre is selling paving slabs for £1.12 each. How much will the slabs cost Gethin altogether? _____

3. Convert $\frac{12}{15}$ into a decimal. _____

4. Convert 0.382 into a fraction and write the answer in its simplest form. _____

5. Convert $\frac{26}{80}$ into a percentage. _____

6. Write the missing numbers to make each line add up to 1148.

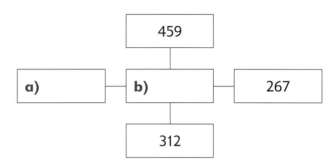

459

a) **b)** 267

312

7. Express each of these ratios in its simplest form.

a) 200cm:1km _____:_____

b) 10 seconds:$1\frac{1}{2}$ minutes _____:_____

c) 450ml:2l _____:_____

8. How many kilograms of hay are needed for 100 horses for 6 weeks if they each eat $\frac{1}{8}$kg of hay a day? _____

9. A train travelled at 120km/hr. How far did it travel in these times?

a) $2\frac{1}{2}$ hours _____

b) 3.25 hours _____

c) 1.2 hours _____

10. The mean mass of 9 cats was 3.2kg. What was their total mass? _____

11. Solve these calculations.

a) 0.45 ÷ 0.3 = _____

b) 0.6125 ÷ 0.25 = _____

c) 0.95 ÷ 0.4 = _____

Score:	Time taken:	Target met?

Target time: **8 minutes**

1. Write the missing numbers in these calculations.

a)

```
    4 ? 2 6
  ×       9
  4 ? 7 ? 4
```

_____

_____ _____

b)

```
      8 ? 2
  7 ) 5 8 9 ?
```

_____

_____

2. Complete the table.

	Distance travelled	Speed	Time taken
a)	156 miles	6 miles/hr	_____ hours
b)	60m	_____ m/min	20 seconds
c)	_____ km	45km/hr	1.5 hours

3. In 12 minutes, a bread factory can make 136 loaves of bread. How many loaves of bread can it make in $3\frac{1}{4}$ hours?

_____

4. Andy, Boris and Charlie work at the local supermarket. The hours they work are in the ratio of 5:3:6. If they work for a total of 168 hours, how many hours does each work?

a) Andy _____

b) Boris _____

c) Charlie _____

5. Calculate the following.

a) If $x^2 + 12 = 61$, $x =$ _____

b) $x + y = 66$. If x is 14 more than y, $y =$ _____

c) If $3b + c = 55$ and c is twice as large as b, what is c? _____

6. The following plan shows Hazel's garden.

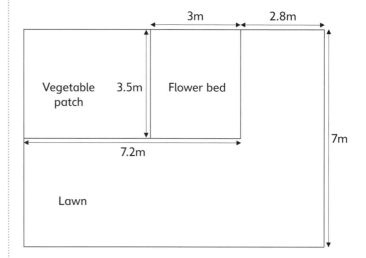

a) What is the area of the lawn? _____

b) Hazel wants to put a wooden border around the entire edge of the lawn. How much edging does she need? _____

c) What fraction of the garden is flower bed? _____

d) Hazel needs to buy fertiliser for the vegetable patch. Each bag covers 4m². How many bags does she need? _____

7. If $\frac{2}{7}$ of a house costs £173 000, what does the house cost? _____

8. Yasmin was the top goal scorer on her netball team. Over 6 matches she scored 8, 12, 5, 9, 13 and 7 goals.

a) What was her mean score? _____

b) What was her median score? _____

c) After 7 matches her mean rose to 10. How many goals did she score in her 7th match? _____

Score:		Time taken:		Target met?	

Target time: **8 minutes**

1. This is a bar chart showing Talin's bank balance over the course of a year.

Bank balance

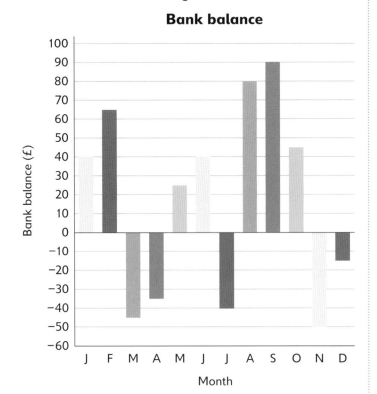

a) For how many months was Talin in debt? _____

b) In which month was his overdraft the greatest? _____

c) How much money did Talin spend between September and October? _____

d) Between which 2 months did his bank balance drop the most?

_____

e) Between which 2 months did his bank balance increase the most?

_____

2. In a football season Archie, Rory and Raj scored a total of 153 goals. If they scored in the ratio of 2:3:4, how many did each boy score?

a) Archie _____

b) Rory _____

c) Raj _____

3. If $3\frac{1}{4}$ litres of orange juice costs £4.55, what does $\frac{1}{2}$ litre cost? _____

4. The sum of three consecutive numbers is 234. What is the smallest of the three numbers? _____

5. What number is halfway between $2\frac{3}{4}$ and $5\frac{1}{2}$? _____

6. Complete the chart showing the selling price of each item.

	Item	Cost price	Profit	Selling price
a)	Ice cream	£1.20	12.5%	
b)	Doughnuts	30p	40%	
c)	Eggs	50p	24%	
d)	Orange juice	80p	45%	
e)	Sausages	£2.50	36%	

7. Ria's watch stopped working properly at 15:34. Instead, it started working at half speed, so for every minute it only moved forwards 30 seconds.

a) If her watch says exactly 15:42, what is the actual time? _____

b) If her watch says exactly 16:56, what is the actual time? _____

c) The actual time is 15:48. What time does Ria's watch say? _____

d) The actual time is 17:26. What time does Ria's watch say? _____

Score: _____   Time taken: _____   Target met? _____

Target time: **8 minutes**

1. **a)** Plot and label the points A (2, 3), B (−2, 3) and C (−1, 6).

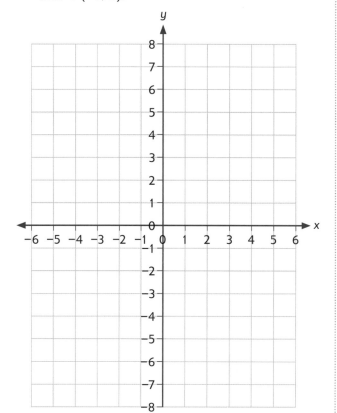

b) These are three points of a trapezium with one line of symmetry. Plot the 4th point, label it D and join points ABCD. Label the shape X.

c) Rotate the shape 90° clockwise about point A. Label the shape Y.

d) Reflect this new shape in the x axis and label it Z.

e) What are the coordinates for shape Z?

(_____ , _____)

(_____ , _____)

(_____ , _____)

(_____ , _____)

2. Write these fractions, decimals and percentages in ascending order.

$\frac{2}{5}$ 0.65 $\frac{3}{8}$ 12.5%   0.42

_____

3. How many seconds are there in $3\frac{1}{4}$ days? _____

4. Ava spent $\frac{5}{8}$ of her money on sweets and $\frac{1}{5}$ of her money on a magazine.

She has 14p left. How much did she start with? _____

5. A square has a perimeter of 15.2cm. What is its area? _____

6. Write the missing number.

64	27	8
125	64	27
	125	64

7. Look at the numbers below. They are the beginning of a sequence.

6, 8, 10, 12

a) What is the formula for the nth term? _____

b) What would the 26th term be? _____

c) What is the value of n when the nth term is 124? _____

8. Solve these calculations.

a) $(5 + 7)^2 \times 6 \div 2 =$ _____

b) $3^3 + 9 \times 8 \div 12 =$ _____

| Score: | | Time taken: | | Target met? | |

Target time: **8 minutes**

1. 5.5cm of wire is needed to make a paper clip. How many paper clips can be made from 10.5m of wire? _____

2. Circle the numbers which are divisible by 3, 5 and 9.

   235   513   225   741   675

3. What is the total length of the edges of a cube with a volume of 125cm³? _____

4. Which multiple of 11 is closest to 1000? _____

5. Complete these sequences.

   a) XII, XVI, XXI, XXVII, _____, _____

   b) 5.6, 6.9, 8.2, 9.5, _____, _____

6. Solve these calculations and write each answer in its simplest form.

   a) $1\frac{3}{4} + \frac{5}{6} =$ _____

   b) $2\frac{1}{2} - 1\frac{3}{5} =$ _____

   c) $\frac{5}{6} \times \frac{1}{3} =$ _____

   d) $\frac{3}{4} \div 10 =$ _____

7. Find the area of this regular pentagon.

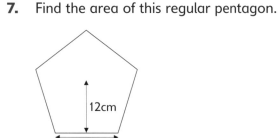

8. Stacey wants to buy a car that costs £6750. She decides to put down a £1050 deposit and then pay by 36 monthly instalments of £175. How much extra will she end up paying by not paying for the car in one go? _____

9. Liam wanted to buy a jacket costing £56. It was reduced by 15% in a sale. What is the new price? _____

10. Trees are planted every 35m along a residential road. What distance is needed to plant 30 trees? Write the answer in kilometres. _____

11. Find the value of x in each of these equations.

    a) $2x + 6 = 3x + 3$ _____

    b) $4x - 4 = 3x + 1$ _____

    c) $6x + 1 = 8x - 3$ _____

12. Round these numbers to two decimal places.

    a) 89.173 _____

    b) 52.629 _____

13. What is the area of the kite?

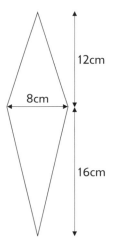

Score: _____   Time taken: _____   Target met? _____

Target time: **8 minutes**

1. Write $\frac{5}{8}$ as a decimal. _____

2. Write 300 as a product of its prime factors. _____

3. Write 54km/hr in metres per second. _____

4. Simplify these formulae.

a) $\frac{6y^2}{3y^2}$ _____

b) $2y^3 + 5y^3$ _____

5. Solve these calculations.

a) $4.5 \div 0.03 =$ _____

b) $0.4 \div 0.05 =$ _____

c) $1.6 \div 0.4 =$ _____

6. Calculate the missing angles in this regular octagon.

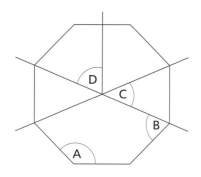

a) A = _____   b) B = _____

c) C = _____   d) D = _____

7. At a nursery, the children each drink $\frac{7}{8}$ of a litre of water a day. If the children drink a total of 22.75 litres a day, how many children are there at the nursery? _____

8. The cost of 3 chicken wraps and 2 drinks is £8.35. The cost of 4 chicken wraps and 4 drinks is £12.20. How much would 1 chicken wrap and 3 drinks cost? _____

9. This line graph shows the mean temperatures in New York and Nuuk.

Temperature comparison

a) What is the difference in temperature in June? _____

b) In which month was the temperature difference the least? _____

c) What is the difference between the highest temperature in New York and the lowest in Nuuk? _____

d) When New York first reaches 20°C, what is the temperature in Nuuk? _____

10. Solve these calculations.

a) $5 \times {-7} =$ _____

b) $-13 - {-16} =$ _____

Score: _____   Time taken: _____   Target met? _____

Progress chart

Write the score (out of 20) for each test in the box provided on the right of the graph.
Then colour in the row next to the box to represent this score.

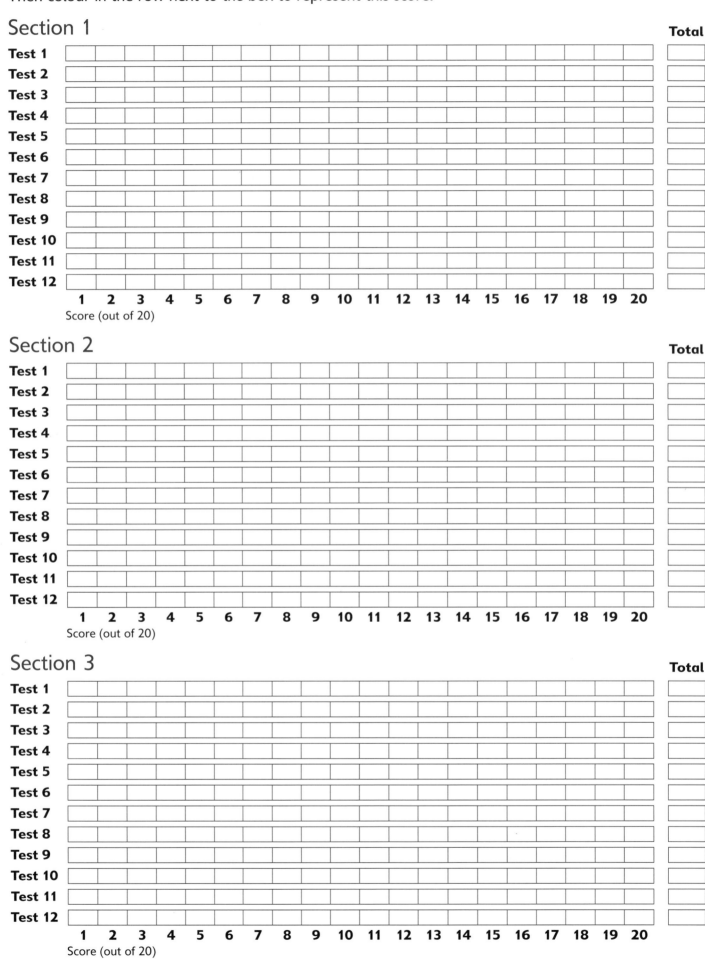

Section 1

		Total
Test 1		
Test 2		
Test 3		
Test 4		
Test 5		
Test 6		
Test 7		
Test 8		
Test 9		
Test 10		
Test 11		
Test 12		

1 2 3 4 5 6 7 8 9 10 11 12 13 14 15 16 17 18 19 20
Score (out of 20)

Section 2

		Total
Test 1		
Test 2		
Test 3		
Test 4		
Test 5		
Test 6		
Test 7		
Test 8		
Test 9		
Test 10		
Test 11		
Test 12		

1 2 3 4 5 6 7 8 9 10 11 12 13 14 15 16 17 18 19 20
Score (out of 20)

Section 3

		Total
Test 1		
Test 2		
Test 3		
Test 4		
Test 5		
Test 6		
Test 7		
Test 8		
Test 9		
Test 10		
Test 11		
Test 12		

1 2 3 4 5 6 7 8 9 10 11 12 13 14 15 16 17 18 19 20
Score (out of 20)